DICTIONARY OF
NANOTECHNOLOGY

DICTIONARY
OF
NANOTECHNOLOGY

G. Whitmore

IVY Publishing House
Delhi—110 095

Published by
IVY Publishing House
Delhi-110095
Sole Distributors
Sarup & Sons
4740/23, Ansari Road
Darya Ganj, New Delhi-110002
Ph.: 011-23281029, 23244664, 41010989
Fax: 011-23277098
email-sarupandsonsin@hotmail.com

Dictionary of Nanotechnology

ISBN 81-7890-156-0
1st Edition 2007
© Reserved

Printed in India

Laser Typesetting at Jain Computers and Printed at Roshan Offset Press, Delhi.

Preface

This dictionary includes simple and basic definitions of concepts, techniques or acronyms relative to nanotechnology, the emerging technology that would probably lead the major 21st century industrial revolution. An attempt has been made to explain each term in a simple language and lucid style. This dictionary is a must for a basic understanding of nanotechnology.

Abstraction reaction
A reaction that removes an atom from a structure.

Ab initio
"From the beginning". Used in computational science to indicate calculations that require no experimental data and only the most basic facts about the system, for example its chemical composition.

ACCOMPANYING MEASURES
Actions supported by the RTD Framework Programmes to contribute to the implementation of a specific programme, with a view to enabling them to achieve or define their strategic objectives. They will also contribute to the preparation of future activities.

Accord
Cheminformatics software products enabling management and analysis of chemical data and information.

ACE Paste
Atomspheric Carbon Extractor. Harvests the greenhouse gases for Carbon, to be used for diamondoid fabrication. Larger than most pastebots, because it has to be collectible afterwards. A well-designed paste could harvest 100X or more its empty weight. ACE Paste may not be necessary, because large fixed installations might be more efficient.

Acid

In the Brønsted definition, an acid is a chemical species that can donate a proton to another species (a base). In the Lewis definition, an acid is a chemical species that can accept (and share) a pair of electrons from another species. Hydrochloric acid is a Brønsted acid; the proton it donates is a Lewis acid. A neutral Lewis acid and a neutral Lewis base can commonly form a dipolar bond.

Acts

Advanced Communications Technologies & Services programme implemented under the Fourth RTD Framework Programme, 1994-98.

Activation energy

Distinct states correspond to minima of a potential energy surface in a configuration space. In this classical picture, the activation energy for transforming state A into state B is the maximum increase in energy (relative to the ground state of A) encountered on a minimum-energy path from A to B. Energy here refers to potential energy; an analogous definition based on free energy can be constructed. When tunneling is considered, lower energy paths become possible, but an activation energy can be associated with the reaction (at a given temperature) via the relationship between temperature and reaction rate.

Acyclic

Not cyclic.

Adensoine Triphosphate [ATP]

A chemical compound that functions as fuel for biomolecular nanotechnology having the formula, $C_{10}H_{16}N_5O_{13}P_3$.

ADME/Tox (Absorption, Distribution, Metabolism and Excretion / Toxicity)

The set of properties related to behavior in the body that are critical to the success of a potential drug. They often cause failures in clinical trials, even where the drug has a desired therapeutic effect.

Adsorbate

A substance which sticks or adsorbs on surfaces. An adsorbate can be a molecule which is used to build up a defined layer by a CVD process for example.

Affinity constant

The reciprocal of the dissociation constant; a measure of the binding energy of a ligand in a receptor.

AFM

An atomic force microscope.

Alkane

A saturated, acyclic hydrocarbon structure; usually quite inert.

Alkene

A hydrocarbon containing a double bond; often rather reactive.

Alkyne

A hydrocarbon containing a triple bond; often rather reactive.

Amide

A molecule containing an amine bonded to a carboxyl group; the resulting bond has substantial double-bond character. Also termed a peptide; amide bonds link amino acids in proteins.

A molecule containing an amine bonded to a carboxyl group.

Amine

A molecule containing N with a single bond to C and two other single bonds to H or C (but not an amide); the amine group or moiety.

Amino acid

A molecule containing both an amine and a carboxylic acid group; in the 20 genetically encoded amino acids in biology, both groups are bound to the same C. Amino acids joined by amide bonds form peptides and proteins; these do not contain amino acids as such, and are instead said to contain amino acid residues.

2. A molecule containing both an amine and a carboxylic acid group.

Amorphous material

Solid materials or liquids where there is no order in the structure. Modeling these systems requires the application of advanced statistical techniques or the use of sophisticated approximations. Examples include many polymer systems.

Analytical instruments

Machines used to measure and analyze the structure or properties of chemicals, biological systems, or materials. They often work by measuring the way in which the sample interacts with radiation: X-rays, infrared, ultra-violet, or light. Software can be vital in interpreting results.

Anchor

Embedded marker enabling authors to link to a specific part of a Web document.

Anion

A negatively charged ion.

Aromatic

A term used to describe cyclic pi-bonded structures of special stability.

Assembler

1. A nano-robotic device controlled by an onboard computer that can use available chemicals to manufacture nanoscale products. It has been proposed that advanced designs could communicate, cooperate, and maneuver to build macroscale products. Assemblers are much more complex, and probably less efficient, than fabricators.

2. In recent popular usage, any nanomachine, usually assumed to offer magical, universal capabilities in an atom-sized package. In the author's usage, any programmable nanomechanical system able to perform a wide range of mechanosynthetic operations. See molecular manipulator, molecular mill.

3. A general-purpose device for molecular manufacturing capable of guiding chemical reactions by positioning molecules. A molecular machine that can be programmed to build virtually any molecular structure or device from simpler chemical building blocks. Analogous to a computer-driven machine shop.

2. A general purpose device for molecular manufacturing capable of guiding chemical reactions by positioning molecules

Associated State

Associated States have entered into an Association Agreement with the Community involving reciprocal rights and obligations. Under FP5, they may participate as non-EU legal entities WITH Community Funding once an Association Agreement is in force. They may include, for example, candidates for EU-Membership or EFTA-EEA Countries. Click here for details of Third Country participation in FP5.

Atom

The smallest unit of a chemical element, about a third of a nanometer in diameter. Atoms make up molecules and solid objects.

Atomic force microscope (AFM)

An instrument able to image surfaces to molecular accuracy by mechanically probing their surface contours. A kind of proximal probe.

2. A device in which the deflection of a sharp stylus mounted on a soft spring is monitored as the stylus is moved across a surface. If the deflection is kept constant by moving the surface up and down by measured increments, the result (under favorable conditions) is an atomic-resolution topographic map of the surface. Also termed a scanning force microscope.

A high-powered instrument able to image surfaces to molecular accuracy by mechanically probing their surface contours.

3. Atomic force microscopy (AFM) is a technique for analyzing the surface topography with a resolution down to the level of the atom. The AFM detects forces acting on a probe which is in mechanical contact with the surface using a small spring

or cantilever. The probe is scanned line by line over the area of interest, whereby the topography is derived from the bending or deflection of the cantilever. The AFM is closely related to another scanning probe technique (SPM), called scanning tunneling microscopy (STM). The difference is that AFM does not require a conductive sample, whereas STM does. AFM is being used to understand materials problems in many areas, including data storage, telecommunications, biomedicine, chemistry, and aerospace.

4. An instrument able to image surfaces to molecular accuracy by mechanically probing their surface contours. A kind of proximal probe. .... A device in which the deflection of a sharp stylus mounted on a soft spring is monitored as the stylus is moved across a surface. If the deflection is kept constant by moving the surface up and down by measured increments, the result (under favorable conditions) is an atomic-resolution topographic map of the surface. Also termed a scanning force microscope.

Atomic Manipulation

Manipulating atoms, typically with the tip of an STM.

Atomistic Simultations

Atomic motion computer simulations of macromolecular systems are increasingly becoming an essential part of materials science and nanotechnology. Recent advances in supercomputer simulation techniques provide the necessary tools for performing computations on nanoscale objects containing as many as 300,000 atoms and on materials simulated with 1,000,000 atoms. This new capability will allow computer simulation of mechanical devices or molecular machines using nanometer size components.

Auger electron

Electron emitted from an core-ionised atom via a two step process. Generally an ionised atom will emit light, when an electron fills the empty place, but under certain conditions the energy will be transferred onto another electron which is emitted with a characteristic energy. This is a competing process to x-ray emissions and can be observed for lighter atoms predominantly. Auger electrons are named after the three atomic shells involved (e.g. KLM).

Auger Electron Spectroscopy (AES)

Surface analytical method revealing the chemical composition. Surface atoms or molecules are core-ionised by an electron beam for instance. The energy of the emitted Auger electrons is recorded providing surface sensitive chemical information.

Automated Engineering

Engineering design done by a computer system, generating detailed designs from broad specifications with little or no human help.

Automated manufacturing

As used here, nanotechnology-based manufacturing requiring little human labor.

Autoproductivity

The ability of a system, under external control, to automatically produce an identical copy of itself.

B

Bacteria
Single-celled microorganisms, about one micrometer (one thousand nanometers) across.

Ballistic Magnetoresistance
(BMR) is yet another way in which spin orientation, encoding information on a storage medium such as a hard drive, can modify electrical resistance in a nearby circuit, thereby accomplishing the sensing of that orientation.

Barrier height
Roughly synonymous with activation energy.

Base
In the Brønsted definition, a base is a chemical species that can accept a proton from another species. In the Lewis definition, a base is a chemical species that can donate (and share) a pair of electrons with another species. See acid.

Bearing
A mechanical device that permits the motion of a component (ideally, with minimal resistance) in one or more degrees of freedom while resisting motion (ideally, with a stiff restoring force) in all other degrees of freedom.

Binding energy
The reduction in the free energy of a system that occurs when

a ligand binds to a receptor. Generally used to describe the total energy required to remove something, or to take a system apart into its constituent particles--for example, to separate two atoms from one another, or to separate an atom into electrons and nuclei.

Binding site
The active region of a receptor; any site at which a chemical species of interest tends to bind.

Binding
The process by which a molecule (or ligand) becomes bound, that is, confined in position (and often orientation) with respect to a receptor. Confinement occurs because structural features of the receptor create a potential well for the ligand; van der Waals and electrostatic interactions commonly contribute.

Bio-assemblies or Biomolecular Assemblies
Containing several protein units, DNA loops, lipids, various ligands, etc.

Biochauvinism
The prejudice that biological systems have an intrinsic superiority that will always give them a monopoly on self-reproduction and intelligence.

Biomimetic
Imitating, copying, or learning from nature. Nanotechnology already exists in nature; thus, nanoscientists have a wide variety of components and tricks already available.

Biomimetics
Study of the structure and function of biological substances to make artificial products that mimic the natural ones.

Biomimetic Chemistry
Knowledge of biochemistry, analytical chemistry, polymer science, and biomimetic chemistry is linked and applied to research in designing new molecules, molecular assemblies, and macromolecules having biomimetic functions. These new

bio-related materials of high performance, including, for example, enzyme models, synthetic cell membranes, and biodegradable polymers, are prepared, tested, and constantly improved in this division for industrial scale production.

Biomimetic Materials
Materials that imitate, copy, or learn from nature.

Biopolymeroptoelectromechanical Systems [BioPOEMS]
Combining optics and microelectromechanical systems, and used in biological applications.

Biostasis
A condition in which an organism's cell and tissue structure are preserved, allowing later restoration by cell repair machines. Applicable to cryonics. [FS] See also "ischemic coma," "ametabolic coma," "biostatic coma," and "in suspension."

Biovorous
From "biovore;" an organism capable of converting biological material into energy for sustenance.

Blue Goo
opposite of Grey goo. Benificial tech, or "police" nanobots.

Bogosity Filter
A mechanism for detecting bogus ideas and propositions.

Bond
Two atoms are said to be bonded when the energy required to separate them is substantially larger than the van der Waals attraction energy. Ionic bonds result from the electrostatic attraction between ions; covalent and metallic bonds result from the sharing of electrons among atoms; hydrogen bonds are weaker and result from dipole interactions and limited electron sharing. When used without modification, "bond" usually refers to a covalent bond.

Born-Oppenheimer Approximation
Permits the use of classical mechanics in modeling and thinking

about molecular and atomic motions. Needless to say, this greatly simplifies the conceptual framework required for thinking about molecular machines. [RCM] Once used as an argument on why MNT could not work. Since refuted: See That's impossible! How good scientists reach bad conclusions.

Bose-Einstein Condensates [BEC's]

"...aren't like the solids, liquids and gases that we learned about in school. They are not vaporous, not hard, not fluid. Indeed, there are no ordinary words to describe them because they come from another world -- the world of quantum mechanics."

Bottom Up

Building larger objects from smaller building blocks. Nanotechnology seeks to use atoms and molecules as those building blocks. The advantage of bottom-up design is that the covalent bonds holding together a single molecule are far stronger than the weak. [NTN] Mostly done by chemists, attempting to create structure by connecting molecules.

Brownian assembly

Brownian motion in a fluid brings molecules together in various positions and orientations. If molecules have suitable complementary surfaces, they can bind, assembling to form a specific structure. Brownian assembly is a less paradoxical name for self-assembly (how can a structure assemble itself, or do anything, when it does not yet exist?).

Brownian motion

Motion of a particle in a fluid owing to thermal agitation, observed in 1827 by Robert Brown. (Originally thought to be caused by a vital force, Brownian motion in fact plays a vital role in the assembly and activity of the molecular structures of life.)

Buckyball or Fullerene or C60

One of three known pure forms of carbon (graphite and diamond being the other two) that takes a spherical shape with a hollow interior. Buckyballs, named because they resemble the geodesic domes built by architect Buckminster

Fuller, were discovered in 1985 among the byproducts of laser vaporization of graphite in which the carbon atoms are arranged in sheets. Though C60, referring to the number of carbon atoms that make up one sphere, is the most common fullerene, researchers have found stable, spherical carbon structures containing 70 atoms (C70), 120 (C120), 180 (C180), and others.

Robert F. Curl Jr. and Richard E. Smalley, both of Rice University in Houston, Texas and Harold W. Kroto of the University of Sussex in England, won the 1996 Nobel Prize for Chemistry for their discovery of buckminsterfullerene, the scientific name for buckyballs.

2. Geodesic spheres named for visionary engineer R. Buckminster Fuller, inventor of the geodesic sphere. Buckyballs are strong, rigid natural molecules arranged in a series of interlocking hexagonal shapes, forming structures that resemble soccer balls. One individual buckyball comprises exactly 60 carbon atoms. In 1996, Richard Smalley received the Nobel Prize in chemistry for his discovery of buckyballs.

Bulk technology
Technology in which atoms and molecular are manipulated in bulk, rather than individually.

Buckminsterfullerene
See Fullerenes. A broad term covering the variety of buckyballs and carbon nanotubes that exist. Named after the architect Buckminster Fuller, who is famous for the geodesic dome, which buckyballs resemble.

Bucky Balls
[AKA: C60 molecules & buckminsterfullerene] - molecules made up of 60 carbon atoms arranged in a series of interlocking hexagonal shapes, forming a structure similar to a soccer ball. See our Nanotubes and Buckyball page.

Bush Robot
A concept for robots of ultimate dexterity, they utilize fractal branching to create ever-shrinking "branches," eventually ending in nanoscale "fingers." Developed by Hans Moravec. See Fractal branching ultra-dexterous robots.

C

CAD
Computer-aided design.

Cam
A component that translates or rotates to move a contoured surface past a follower; the contours impose a sequence of motions (potentially complex) on the follower.

Carbanion
A highly reactive anionic chemical species with an even number of electrons and an unshared pair of electrons on a tetravalent carbon atom.

Carbene
A highly reactive chemical species containing an electrically neutral, divalent carbon atom with two nonbonding valence electrons; a prototype is CH_2.

Carbon Nanotubes
A form of carbon related to fullerenes, except that the carbon atoms form extended hollow tubes instead of closed, hollow spheres. Carbon nanotubes can also form as a series of nested, concentric tubes. Carbon nanotubes can be used as nanometer-scale syringe needles for injecting molecules into cells and as nanoscale probes for making fine-scale measurements. Carbon nanotubes can be filled and capped, forming nanoscale test

tubes or potential drug delivery devices. Carbon nanotubes can also be "doped," or modified with small amounts of other elements, giving them electrical properties that include fully insulating, semiconducting, and fully conducting.

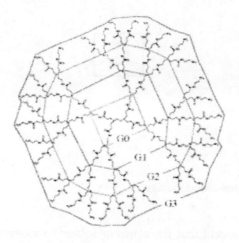

Carbonium ion
A highly reactive cationic chemical species with an even number of electrons and an unoccupied orbital on a carbon atom.

Carbonyl
A chemical moiety consisting of O with a double bond to C. If the C is bonded to N, the resulting structure is termed an amide; if it is bonded to O, it is termed a carboxylic acid or an ester linkage.

Carboxylic acid
A molecule that includes a C having a double bond to O and a single bond to OH.

Catalyst
A chemical species or other structure that facilitates a chemical reaction without itself undergoing a permanent change.

Cation
A positively charged ion.

Cell pharmacology
Delivery of drugs by medical nanomachines to exact locations in the body.

Cell Repair Machine
Molecular and nanoscale machines with sensors, nanocomputers and tools, programmed to detect and repair damage to cells and tissues, which could even report back to and receive instructions from a human doctor if needed.

Multiple Cell Repair Units Working Together

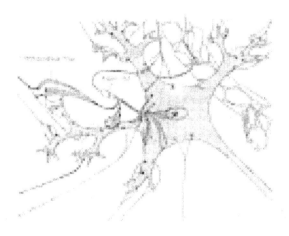

Several cell repair units are shown simultaneously engaged in repairing a single neuronal cell. Communications fibers and cables link the repair units to a master controller system that directs all the repair activities from outside the scene.

Cell surgery
Modifying cellular structures using medical nanomachines.

Cell

A small structural unit, surrounded by a membrane, making up living things.

Cellular Automata

An array of identically programmed automata, or "cells," which interact with one another.

Chemical Vapour Deposition (CVD)

A technique used to deposit coatings, where chemicals are first vaporized, and then applied using an inert carrier gas such as nitrogen.

Classical mechanics

Classical mechanics describes a mechanical system as a set of particles (which in a limiting case can form continuous media) having a well-defined geometry at any given time, and undergoing motions determined by applied forces and by the initial positions and velocities of the particles. The forces themselves may have electromagnetic or quantum mechanical origins. Classical statistical mechanics uses the same physical model, but treats the geometry and velocities as uncertain, statistical quantities subject to random thermally-induced fluctuations. Classical mechanics and classical statistical mechanics give a good account of many mechanical properties and behaviors of molecules; but for describing the electronic properties and behaviors of molecules, they are often useless.

CMOS

An acronym for complementary metal-oxide-semiconductor, as in CMOS transistor and CMOS logic.

Cobots

Collaborative robots designed to work alongside human operators. Prototype cobots are being used on automobile assembly lines to help guide heavy components like seats and dashboards into cars so they don't damage auto body parts as workers install them.

Cognotechnology

Convergence of nanotech, biotech and IT, for remote brain sensing and mind control.

Col

In describing landforms, a pass between two valleys is sometimes termed a col. In describing molecular potential energy functions, this term is commonly used to describe analogous features of the PES; a col is the region around a saddle point having negative curvature along one axis and positive curvature along all orthogonal axes.

Compliance

The reciprocal of stiffness; in a linear elastic system, displacement equals force times compliance.

Computational Nanotechnology

Permits the modeling and simulation of complex nanometer-scale structures. The predictive and analytical power of computation is critical to success in nanotechnology: nature required several hundred million years to evolve a functional "wet" nanotechnology; the insight provided by computation should allow us to reduce the development time of a working "dry" nanotechnology to a few decades, and it will have a major impact on the "wet" side as well.

Computronium

A highly (or optimally) efficient matrix for computation, such as dense lattices of nanocomputers or quantum dot cellular automata.

Configuration space

A mathematical space describing the three-dimensional configuration of a system of particles (e.g., atoms in a nanomechanical structure) as a single point; the configuration space for an N particle system has 3N dimensions.

Conformation

A molecular geometry that differs from other geometries chiefly by rotation about single or triple bonds; distinct conformations (termed con formers) are associated with distinct potential wells. Typical biomolecules and products of organic synthesis can interconvert among many conformations; typical diamondoid structures are locked into a single potential well, and thus lack conformational flexibility.

Conjugated

A conjugated pi system is one in which pi bonds alternate with single bonds. The resulting electron distribution gives the intervening single bonds partial double-bond character, the pi electrons become delocalized, and the energy of the system is reduced.

Conservative

In design and analysis, a conservative model or a conservative assumption is one that departs from accuracy in such a way that it reduces the chances of a false-positive assessment of the feasibility of the system in question. Conservative assumptions overestimate problems and underestimate capabilities.

Contelligence

(Consciousness + intelligence) The combination of awareness and computational power required in an Artificially Intelligent network before we could, without loss of anything essential, upload ourselves into them.

Convergent Assembly

"...rapidly make products whose size is measured in meters starting from building blocks whose size is measured in nanometers. It is based on the idea that smaller parts can be assembled into larger parts, larger parts can be assembled into still larger parts, and so forth. This process can be systematically repeated in a hierarchical fashion, creating an architecture able to span the size range from the molecular to the macroscopic."

Covalent bond

A bond formed by sharing a pair of electrons between two atoms.

Covalent radius

Given a set of N elements that can form covalent single bonds in molecules, with $N(N - 1)$ possible elemental pairings, it has proved possible to define a covalent radius for each element such that the actual bond length between any two elements that form a covalent single bond is roughly equal to the sums of their covalent radii.

Convergent assembly

A process of fastening small parts to obtain larger parts, then fastening those to make still larger parts, and so on; convergent assembly can be used to build a product from many, much smaller, components.

CPU

The central processing unit of a computer, responsible for executing instructions to process information.

Cyclic

A structure is termed cyclic if its covalent bonds form one or more rings.

Cycloaddition

A reaction in which two unsaturated molecules (or moieties within a molecule) join, forming a ring.

D

Dative bond

A dipolar bond.

Dendrimer

A dendrimer is a tree-like highly branched polymer molecule (Greek *dendra* = *tree*). Dendrimers are synthesized from monomers with new branches added in discrete steps ("generation") to form a tree-like architecture. A high level of synthetic control is achieved through step-wise reactions and purifications at each step to control the size, architecture, functionality and monodispersity. Several different kinds of dendrimers have been synthesized utilizing different monomers and some are commercially available. This picture shows a "3rd generation" polyamidoamine (PAMAM) dendrimer.

2. From the Greek word dendra - tree, a dendrimer is polymer that branches. [Encyclopedia Nanotech] "...a tiny molecular structure that interacts with cells, enabling scientists to probe, diagnose, cure or manipulate them on a nanoscale." Invented by Professor Donald Tomalia from Central Michigan University. [SmallTimes] See this article for a great explanation Dendrimers: Branching out into new realms of molecular architecture.

Design Ahead

The use of known principles of science and engineering to design systems that can only be built with tools not yet available; this permits faster exploitation of the abilities of new tools.

Design Diversity

A form of redundancy in which components of different design serve the same purpose; this can enable systems to function properly despite design flaws.

Diamondoid

Structures that resemble diamond in a broad sense, strong stiff structures containing dense, three dimensional networks of covalent bonds; diamondoid materials could be as much as 100 to 250 times as strong as titanium, and far lighter.

2. As used in this volume, this term describes structures that resemble diamond in a broad sense: strong, stiff structures containing dense, three-dimensional networks of covalent bonds, formed chiefly from first and second row atoms with a valence of three or more. Many of the most useful diamondoid structures will in fact be rich in tetrahedrally coordinated carbon. Diamondoid is used more narrowly elsewhere in the literature.

3. Stuctures that resemble diamond in a broad sense, strong stiff structures containing dense, three dimensional networks of covalent bonds, formed chiefly from first and second row atoms with a valence of three or more. Many of the most useful diamondoid structures will in fact be rich in tetrahedrally coordinated carbon. [NTN] Materials with superior strength to weight ratio, as much as 100 to 250 times as strong as Titanium, and much lighter. Possibly used to build stronger lighter rockets and space components, or a variety of other earth-bound articles for which weight and strength are a consideration.

4. Stuctures that resemble diamond in a broad sense, strong stiff structures containing dense, three dimensional networks of covalent bonds, formed chiefly from first and second row atoms with a valence of three or more. Many of the most useful diamondoid structures will in fact be rich in tetrahedrally coordinated carbon .

Dipolar bond

A covalent bond in which one atom supplies both bonding

electrons, and the other atom supplies an empty orbital in which to share them. Also termed a dative bond.

Dip Pen Nanolithography

An AFM-based soft-lithography technique. See example at Surface science in the Mirkin Group.

Directed-Assembler

A specific type of assembler that makes use of directed-assembly, such that the assembly process requires external energy or information input.

Disassembler

An instrument able to take apart structures a few atoms at a time, recording structural information at each step.
2. An instrument able to take apart structures a few atoms at a time, recording structural information at each step. This could be used for uploading, copying objects (with an assembler), a dissolving agent or a weapon.

Dissociation constant

For systems in which ligands of a particular kind bind to a receptor in a solvent there will be a characteristic frequency with which existing ligand-receptor complexes dissociate as a result of thermal excitation, and a characteristic frequency with which empty receptors bind ligands as a result of Brownian encounters, forming new complexes. The frequency of binding is proportional to the concentration of the ligand in solution. The dissociation constant is the magnitude of the ligand concentration at which the probability that the receptor will be found occupied is $1/2$.

Disasterbation

Idly fantasizing about possible catastrophes (ecological collapse, full-blown totalitarianism) without considering their likelihood or considering their possible solutions and preventions.

Disruptive Technology

Technology that is significantly cheaper than current, is much higher performing, has greater functionality, and is frequently more convenient to use. Will revolutionize markets by superseding existing technology. "Paradigm shifting" is a well-worn connotation. Although the term may sound negative to some, it is in fact neutral. It is only negative when businesses who are unprepared for change fail to adapt, only to fall behind and fail. The results are not evolutionary, they are revolutionary.

Distributed Intelligence

An intelligent entity which is distributed over a large volume (or inside another system, like a computer network) with no distinct center. This is the opposite to the strategy of Concentrated intelligences. Distributed intelligences have much longer communications lags, but are more flexible in their structure and can survive damage to their parts.

DNA

A molecule encoding genetic information, found in the cell's nucleus.

DNA Chip

Gene Chip and DNA Microchip. A purpose built microchip used to identify mutations or alterations in a gene's DNA. See DNA Chip Technology.

Dopeyballs

Superconducting Buckyballs (they) have the highest critical temperature of any known organic compound.

Double bond

Two atoms sharing electrons as in a single bond (that is, a sigma bond) may also share electrons in an orbital with a node passing through the two atoms. This adds a second, weaker bonding interaction (a pi bond); the combination is termed a double bond. A twisting motion that forces the nodal plane at one atom to become perpendicular to the nodal plane on the other atom eliminates the (signed) overlap between the atomic orbitals, destroying the pi bond. The energy required to do this creates a large barrier to rotation about the bond (see triple bond).

Doublet

The electronic state of a molecule having one unpaired spin is termed a doublet (see radical). This term is derived from spectroscopy: an unpaired spin can be either up or down with respect to a magnetic field, and these states have different energy, resulting in field-dependent pairs, or doublets, of spectral lines. (See triplet, singlet.)

Dry Nanotechnology

Derives from surface science and physical chemistry, focuses on fabrication of structures in carbon (e.g. fullerenes and nanotubes), silicon, and other inorganic materials. Unlike the "wet" technology, "dry" techniques admit use of metals and semiconductors. The active conduction electrons of these materials make them too reactive to operate in a "wet" environment, but these same electrons provide the physical properties that make "dry" nanostructures promising as electronic, magnetic, and optical devices. Another objective is to develop "dry" structures that possess some of the same attributes of the self-assembly that the wet ones exhibit.

DumbSizing

Apealing to the least common denominator by explaining difficult concepts in such a manner so they loose meaning. Also, talking down to someone less informed or learned.

Dyson Scenario, the

Life expands into the universe, which is open. As the universe cools, life stores energy to survive (do information processing). It waits until the universe is cool enough, performs some processing with part of its energy stores, then waits until the universe has cooled so much that the remaining energy can be used to do an equal amount of computation, and so on. Essentially life has to adapt as the universe grows older, changing itself to be able to survive when the stars grow cold. If the universe is open, there will be plenty of time to work in, but energy will become very scarce. Dyson has shown that a finite amount of energy is enough to guarantee infinite survival if it is spent sufficiently slowly.

Dyson Sphere

A shell built around a star to collect as much energy as possible, originally proposed by Freeman Dyson (although he admits to have borrowed the concept from Olaf Stapledon's novel Star Maker (1937)). In the original proposal the shell consists of many independent solar collectors and habitats in separate orbits (also known as a Type I Dyson Sphere), but later people have discussed rigid shells consisting of only one piece (called a Type II Dyson Sphere). The latter construction is unfortunately both unstable (since it will experience no net attraction of the star), requires super-strong materials and have no internal gravity. The Dyson Sphere is a classic example of mega-technology and common in Science Fiction.

Ecophagy

(or Global Ecophagy) Consuming the biological environment. Coined and defined by Robert A. Freitas Jr. (Research Scientist Zyvex Corp). Frequently associated with "gray goo," as ecophagy (uncontrolled self-replication) is its main prupose. See "Some Limits to Global Ecophagy by Biovorous Nanoreplicators, with Public Policy Recommendations" where Dr. Freitas said "Perhaps the earliest-recognized and best-known danger of molecular nanotechnology is the risk that self-replicating nanorobots capable of functioning autonomously in the natural environment could quickly convert that natural environment (e.g., "biomass") into replicas of themselves (e.g., "nanomass") on a global basis, a scenario usually referred to as the 'gray goo problem' but perhaps more properly termed 'global ecophagy.'"

Ecosystem protector

A nanomachine for mechanically removing selected imported species from an ecosystem to protect native species.

Effective mass

In a vibrating system, a particular vibrational mode can be described as a harmonic oscillator with some mass and stiffness. Given some measure of vibrational amplitude, there exists a unique choice of mass and stiffness that yields the correct values for both frequency and energy; these are the effective mass and effective stiffness.

Effective stiffness
See effective mass.

Elastic
An object behaves elastically if it returns to its original shape after a force is applied and then removed. (If an applied force causes a permanent deformation, the behavior is termed plastic.) In an elastic system, the internal potential energy is a function of shape alone, independent of past forces and deformations.

Electrical Bistability
A phenomenon in which an object exhibits two states of different conductivity at the same applied voltage.

Electron density
The location of an electron is not fixed, but is instead described by a probability density function. The sum of the probability densities of all the electrons in a region is the electron density in that region.

Electronegativity
A measure of the tendency of an atom (or moiety) to withdraw electrons from structures to which it is bonded. In most circumstances, for example, sodium tends to donate electron density (it has a low electronegativity) and fluorine tends to withdraw electron density (it has a high electronegativity).

Electronic
Pertaining to the energies, distributions, and behaviors of electrons; see mechanical.

Emergence
A complex whole created by simple parts, as in the brain where billions of neurons work individually, but collectively make up our consciousness and give us the ability to think, rationalize, and create.

EI - Emergent Intelligence
An intelligent system that gradually emerges from simpler systems, instead of being designed top down.

Emulation

An absolutely precise simulation of something, so exact that it is equivalent to the original (for example, many computers emulate obsolete computers to run their programs).

Enabling science and technologies

Areas of research relevant to a particular goal, such as nanotechnology.

2. Areas of research relevant to a particular goal, such as nanotechnology. [FS] Also, technology that "enables" other technology to advance, such as the transistor enabled the computer chip revolution, as did photolithography.

Endoergic

A transformation is termed endoergic if it absorbs energy; such a reaction increases molecular potential energy. (Sometimes wrongly equated to the narrower term endothermic.)

Endothermic

A transformation is termed endothermic if it absorbs energy in the form of heat. A typical endothermic reaction increases both entropy and molecular potential energy (and is thus analogous to a gas expanding while absorbing heat and compressing a spring).

Energy

A conserved quantity that can be interconverted among many forms, including kinetic energy, potential energy, and electromagnetic energy. Sometimes defined as "the capacity to do work," but in an environment at a uniform nonzero temperature, thermal energy does not provide this capacity. (Note, however, that all energy has mass, and thus can be used to do work by virtue of its gravitational potential energy; this caveat, however, is of no practical significance unless a really deep gravity well is available.)

Entanglement

From quantum mechanics, entanglement is a relationship between two objects in which they both exhibit superposition but once the state of one object is measured, the state of the other is also known.

Enthalpy

The enthalpy of a system is its actual energy (termed the internal energy) plus the product of its volume and the external pressure. Though sometimes termed "heat content," the enthalpy in fact includes energy not contained in the system. Enthalpy proves convenient for describing processes in gases and liquids in laboratory environments, if one does not wish to account explicitly for energy stored in the atmosphere by work done when a system expands. It is of little use, however, in describing processes in nanomechanical systems, where work can take many forms: internal energy is then more convenient. Enthalpy is to energy what the Gibbs free energy is to the Helmholtz free energy.

Entropy

A measure of uncertainty regarding the state of a system: for example, a gas molecule at an unknown location in a large volume has a higher entropy than one known to be confined to a smaller volume. Free energy can be extracted in converting a low-entropy state to a high-entropy state: the (time-average) pressure exerted by a gas molecule can do useful work as a small volume is expanded to a larger volume. In the classical configuration space picture, any molecular system can be viewed as a single-particle gas in a high-dimensional space. In the quantum mechanical picture, entropy is described as a function of the probabilities of occupancy of different members of a set of alternative quantum states. Increased information regarding the state of a system reduces its entropy and thereby increases its free energy, as shown by the resulting ability to extract more work from it. An illustrative contradiction in the simple textbook view of entropy as a local property of a material (defining an entropy per mole, and so forth) can be shown as follows: The third law of thermodynamics states that a perfect crystal at absolute zero has zero entropy*; this is true regardless of its size. A piece of disordered material, such as a glass, has some finite entropy $G_0 > 0$ at absolute zero. In the local-property view, N pieces of glass, even (or especially) if all are atomically identical, must have an entropy of NG0. If these N pieces of glass are arranged in a regular three-dimensional lattice, however, the resulting structure constitutes a perfect crystal (with a large unit cell); at absolute zero, the third law states that this crystal has zero entropy, not NG0. To understand the informational perspective on entropy, it is a useful exercise to consider (1) what the actual entropy of such crystal is as a function of N, with and without information describing the structure of the unit cell, (2) how the third law can be phrased more precisely, and (3) what this more precise statement implies for the entropy of well-defined aperiodic structures. Note that any one unit cell in the crystal can be regarded as a description of all the rest.

2. A measure of the disorder of a closed system. The second law of thermodynamics states that the entropy (and disorder) increases as time moves forward.

Enzymes

Molecular machines found in nature, made of protein, which can catalyze (speed up) chemical reactions.

A protein molecule that acts as a specific catalyst, binding to other molecules in a manner that facilitates a particular chemical reaction.

Equilibrium

A system is said to be at equilibrium (with respect to some set of feasible transformations) if it has minimal free energy. A system containing objects at different temperatures is in disequilibrium, because heat flow can reduce the free energy. Springs have equilibrium lengths, reactants and products in solution have equilibrium concentrations, thermally excited systems have equilibrium probabilities of occupying various states, and so forth.

Ester

A molecule containing an ester linkage, a carbonyl group bonded to an O that is in turn bonded to a C.

Ether

A molecule containing a C-O-H double bond to another O,

making this part of an ester linkage, or some other exception holds).

Eutactic

Characterized by precise molecular order, like that of a perfect crystal, the interior of a protein molecule, or a machine-phase system; contrasted to the disorder of bulk materials, solution environments, or biological structures on a cellular scale. Borderline cases can be identified, but perfection is not necessary. As a crystal with sparse defects is best described as a crystal (rather than as amorphous), so a eutactic structure with sparse defects is best described as (imperfectly) eutactic, rather than as disordered.

Excluded volume

The presence of one molecule (or moiety) reduces the volume available for other molecules (or moieties); resulting reductions in their entropy are termed excluded volume effects.

Exoergic

The opposite of endoergic; describes a transformation that releases energy.

Exothermic

The opposite of endothermic; describes an exoergic transformation in which energy is released as heat. Exoergic reactions in solution are commonly exothermic.

Exploratory engineering

Design and analysis of systems that are theoretically possible but cannot be built yet, owing to limitations in available tools.

Exponential assembly

A manufacturing architecture starting with a single tiny robotic arm on a surface. This first robotic arm makes a second robotic arm on a facing surface by picking up miniature parts ó carefully laid out in advance in exactly the right locations so the tiny robotic arm can find them ó and assembling them. The two robotic arms then make two more robotic arms, one on each of the two facing surfaces. These four robotic arms, two on each surface, then make four more robotic arms. This process continues with the number of robotic arms steadily increasing in the pattern 1, 2, 4, 8, 16, 32, 64, etc. until some manufacturing limit is reached (both surfaces are completely covered with tiny robotic arms, for example). This is an exponential growth rate, hence the name exponential assembly.

Exponential Growth

Inaccurately referred to as "self-replication," exponential growth refers to the process of growth or replication involving doubling within a given period.

Evolution

A process in which a population of self-replicating entities undergoes variation, with successful variants spreading and becoming the basis for further variation.

F

Fabricator

A small nano-robotic device that can use supplied chemicals to manufacture nanoscale products under external control. Fabricators could work together to build macroscale products by convergent assembly. Similar to assemblers, but less complex, easier to build, and probably more efficient.

Fail-stop

Describes a component or subsystem that, in the event of a failure, produces no output (e.g., of material or data) rather than producing a damaged or incorrect output.

Fault-tolerant

Describes a system that can suffer failure in a component or subsystem, yet continue to function correctly.

Femtometer

[abbr: fm] a unit suitable to express the size of atomic nuclei. One quadrillionth (10 to minus 15) of a meter.

Femtosecond

is one quadrillionth of a second, and is to a second what a second is to 32,700,000 years. At 186,000 miles per second, in one femtosecond light travels only far enough to traverse about 1,000 silicon atoms. When used to time a laser pulse, it allows for ultra-precise micromachining, with virtually no damage to surrounding material.

Femtotechnology

The art of manipulating materials on the scale of elementary particles (leptons, hadrons, and quarks). [CA-B] The next step smaller after picotechnology, which is the next step smaller after nanotechnology.

Feynman

Nanotechnology traces its roots to the pioneering work of physicist Richard Feynman. In 1959, Feynman delivered a landmark speech in which he proposed a link between biology and manufacturing. He explained how biological cells manufacture substances. Feynman urged his audience "to consider the possibility that we, too, can make a thing very small, which does what we want-that we can manufacture an object than maneuvers at that level."

Fluidic Self Assembly

A novel technique for accurately assembling large numbers of very small devices. The small size, planarity, and accuracy of the assembly also result in very low parasitic interconnects, comparable to on die traces. This massively parallel assembly process combines the capability and flexibility of assembly with the cost effectiveness of integration.

Invented by Mr. Mark Hadley and was part of his Ph.D. dissertation while he was studying at University of California, Berkley. The FSA process became the foundation for the origins of a new company named Alien Technology Corporation. In the FSA process, specifically shaped semiconductor devices ranging in size from 10 microns to several hundred microns are suspended in liquid and flowed over a surface which has correspondingly shaped "holes" or receptors on it and into which the devices settle. The shape of the devices and of the holes is designed so that the devices fall easily into place and are selfaligning. Alien has successfully demonstrated the assembly of tens of thousands of devices in a single process step. <!--[Seminar Subject: Fluidic Self Assembly Process] -->See Alien Technology White Paper PDF & Fluidic Self Assembly as an enabling technology.

Follower

A component in a cam system that is driven through a pattern of displacements as it rests against a moving contoured surface.

Foglet

A mesoscale machine. A discreet component of utility fog.

Fractal.

A mathematical construct that has a fractional dimension. [Encyclopedia Nanotech] See Fractal Geometry - A Simple Explanation and these Fractal eXtreme Gallery & Fractal Domains for examples [images] and software to create your own.

Fractal Mechatronic Universal Assembler

(or Fractal Assembler) is a machine that is capable of assembling any chemical from a generic descriptions of the properties required of the chemical. The machine comprises of test tube arrays and software linked to robotic cubes and sensor arrays to implement automated mixing and testing to conduct materials research activity.

Fractal Robots

AKA: Fractal Shape Shifting Robots and Programmable "Digital Matter", are programmable machines that can do unlimited tasks in the physical world, the world of matter. Load the right software and the same "machines" can vacuum the carpet, paint your car, or construct an office building and later, wash that building's windows. This is the beginning of "Digital Matter".

Fractal Shape Shifting Robots look like "Rubic's Cubes" that can "slide" over each other on command, changing and moving in any overall shape desired for a particular task. These cubes communicate with each other and share power through simple internal induction coils (or surface contacts in some models), have batteries, a small computer and various kinds of internal magnetic and electric inductive motors (depending on size) used to move over other cubes.

When sufficiently miniaturized (below 0.1mm) and fabricated using photolithography and E-Beam methods, the machines may exceed human manual dexterity and could then be programmed to assemble complex fractal aggregates or even to maintain the photolithographic and E-Beam equipment itself! The ultimate goal is self sustaining systems and "self-assembly" features that can drop cost dramatically and enable successive generations of robots exhibiting greater utility and value, to be built along the way.

Free energy

Free energy is a measure of the ability of a system to do work, such that a reduction in free energy could in principle yield an equivalent quantity of work. The Helmholtz free energy describes the free energy within a system; the Gibbs free energy does not.

Free radical

A radical.

Fullerene

A molecular form of pure carbon that was discovered in 1985. They are cage-like structures of carbon atoms.

2. Fullerenes are a molecular form of pure carbon discovered in 1985. They are cage-like structures of carbon atoms, the most abundant form produced is buckminsterfullerene (C60), with 60 carbon atoms arranged in a spherical structure. There are larger fullerenes containing from 70 to 500 carbon atoms. [Wid] What are fullerenes? A very good explanation, even though some of the translation is a bit rough. See also What are fullerenes?

Gate

In digital logic, a component that can switch the state of an output dependent on the states of one or more inputs.

Genetic Algorithm

Any algorithm which seeks to solve a problem by considering numerous possibilities at once, ranking them according to some standard of fitness, and then combining ("breeding") the fittest in some way. In other words, any algorithm which imitates natural selection.

GENIE

An AI combined with an assembler or other universal constructor, programmed to build anything the owner wishes. Sometimes called a Santa Machine. This assumes a very high level of AI and nanotechnology.

Giant Magnetoresistance: (GMR)

It results from subtle electron-spin effects in ultra-thin 'multilayers' of magnetic materials, which cause huge changes in their electrical resistance when a magnetic field is applied. GMR is 200 times stronger than ordinary magnetoresistance. [See Spintronics and Giant Magneto Resistance] GMR enables sensing of significantly smaller magnetic fields, which in turn allows hard disk storage capacity to increase by a factor of 20.

Gibbs free energy

The Gibbs free energy is the Helmholtz free energy plus the product of the system volume and the external pressure. Changes in the Gibbs free energy at a constant pressure thus include work done against external pressure as a system undergoes volumetric changes. This proves convenient for describing equilibria in gases and liquids at a constant pressure (e.g., at one atmosphere), but is of little use in describing machine-phase chemical processes. Changes in the Gibbs free energy caused by a change in the applied pressure (at constant volume) have no direct physical significance. (See also enthalpy.)

Golden Goo

Another member of the grey goo family of nanotechnology disaster scenarios. The idea is to use nanomachines to filter gold from seawater. If this process got out of control we would get piles of golden goo (the "Wizard's Apprentice Problem"). This scenario demonstrates the need of keeping populations of self-replicating machines under control; it is much more likely than grey goo, but also more manageable.

Gray goo

The name given to free-range self-replicating miniature machines that could, in theory, run out of control and cause severe damage to the biosphere. The actual threat is generally overrated, as we explain here.
2. Gray Goo or Grey Goo - destructive nanobots [AKA: "gray dust"]. opposite of Blue Goo. See Star Trek scenario. Vast legions of destructive nanites. Typically, created by accident. Left unchecked, they will basically convert everthing they contact into more of themselves, or consume and digest it for energy. Either way, its pretty much bad news. The debate rages on.
Also - Self-replicating (von Neumann) nanomachines spreading uncontrolably, building copies of themselves using all available material. This is a commonly mentioned nanotechnology disaster scenario, although it is rather unlikely due to energy constraints and elemental abundances. More probable disaster scenarios are the green goo, golden goo, red

goo, khaki goo scenarios. As a protection blue goo has been proposed.

Green Goo
Nanomachines or bio-engineered organisms used for population control of humans, either by governments or eco-terrorist groups. Would most probably work by sterilizing people through otherwise harmless infections. See Nick Szabo's essay Green Goo -- Life in the Era of Humane Genocide.

Ground state
The lowest-energy state of a system. The electronic ground state of a system cannot reduce its energy by an electronic transition, but may contain vibrational energy (kinetic and potential energy associated with the motions and positions of its atoms); extended systems at ordinary temperatures are always vibrationally excited, and so "ground state" is often taken to mean "electronic ground state."

Group
A set of linked atoms in a molecule; a defined substructure. Typically, a set that is usefully regarded as a unit in chemical reactions of interest.

Group velocity
In wave propagation, the speed of the waveform (e.g., of a peak) can be different from the speed of a group of waves (e.g., of a set of ripples in water). The latter is the group velocity, and is the speed of propagation of information and wave energy. The waveform speed is the phase velocity.

Guy Fawkes Scenario
If nanotechnology becomes widely available, it might become trivial for anyone to committ acts of terrorism (such as making nanomachines build a large amount of explosives under government buildings a la Guy Fawkes). This would either force strict control over nanotechnology (hard) or a decentralized mode of organization.

Harmonic oscillator

A system in which a mass is subject to a linear restoring force, like an ideal spring. A harmonic oscillator vibrates at a fixed frequency, independent of amplitude.

Heat

As defined in thermodynamics, heat is the energy that flows between two systems as a result of temperature differences (a system contains neither heat nor work, but can produce heat or do work). Heat thus differs from thermal energy.

Heat capacity

The ratio of the heat input to the temperature increase in a system. Note that this definition does not imply that a system contains heat, despite the name heat capacity.

Helmholtz free energy

The internal energy of a system minus the product of its entropy and temperature; see free energy.

Heteronuclear

Consisting of different elements.

Hydrocarbon

A molecule consisting only of H and C.

Hydrogen bond

A hydrogen atom covalently bound to an electronegative

atom (e.g., nitrogen, oxygen) has a significant positive charge and can form a weak bond to another electronegative atom; this is termed a hydrogen bond.

Hydrophobic force

Water molecules are linked by a network of hydrogen bonds. A nonpolar, nonwetting, surface (e.g., wax) cannot form hydrogen bonds. To form their full complement of hydrogen bonds, the nearby water molecules must form a more orderly (hence lower entropy) network. This both increases free energy and causes forces that tend to draw hydrophobic surfaces together across distances of several nanometers.

Imaging Contrast Agent

A molecule or molecular complex that increases the intensity of the signal detected by an imaging technique, including MRI and ultrasound. An MRI contrast agent, for example, might contain gadolinium attached to a targeting antibody. The antibody would bind to a specific target – a metastatic melanoma cell, for example – while the gadolinium would increase the magnetic signal detected by the MRI scanner.

Immune machines

Medical nanomachines designed for internal use, especially in the bloodstream and digestive tract, able to identify and disable intruders such as bacteria and viruses.

IMP

Electronic implant, especially in the brain.

Inline Universities

(as opposed to online universities), nanocomputer implants serving to increase intelligence and education of their owners, essentially turning them into walking universities.

Intermolecular

Describes an interaction (e.g., a chemical reaction) between different molecules.

Internal energy

The sum of the kinetic and potential energies (including electromagnetic field energies) of the particles that make up a system.

Intelligent Agent

Aka "software agent". Software that can do things without supervision, because it knows your patterns, history, preferences, likes, dislikes, and so forth. You want to take a vacation - it knows that you really enjoyed that trip to Hawaii, and that you prefer to fly at night, 1st class. It also knows that the bungalow you rented last time was marked as being 5-star, and worth a re-visit. Your IA then collates all your parameters, searches the internet for flights, car rentals, restaurant reservations, and lodgings, and schedules everything for you, with options on the side. No more travel agent - you have a software agent to handle things! Many experts agree that by 2010 we will each have one, and that they will greatly reduce our daily load of trivial and redundant tasks. See Is There an Intelligent Agent in Your Future?.

IA

Intelligence Amplification: Technologies seeking to increase the cognitive abilities of people.

Intramolecular

Describes an interaction (e.g., a chemical reaction) within a single molecule. Intramolecular interactions between widely separated parts of a molecule resemble intermolecular interactions in most respects.

Ion

An atom or molecule with a net charge.

Ionic bond

A chemical bond resulting chiefly from the electrostatic attraction between positive and negative ions.

Isoelectronic

Two molecules are described as isoelectronic if they have the same number of valence electrons in similar orbitals, although they may differ in their distribution of nuclear charges (e.g., H-C N and H-N+ C-. KineticPertaining to the rates of chemical reactions. A fast reaction is said to have fast kinetics; if the balance of products in a reaction is controlled by reaction rates rather than by thermodynamic equilibria, the reaction is said to be kinetically controlled.

J

Jupiter-Brain

A posthuman being of extremely high computational power and size. This is the archetypal concentrated intelligence. The term originated due to an idea by Keith Henson that nanomachines could be used to turn the mass of Jupiter into computers running an upgraded version of himself.

Khaki Goo
Military nanotechnology; see grey goo.

Kinetic energy
Energy resulting from the motion of masses.

Knowbots
Knowledge robots, first developed Vinton G. Cref and Robert E. Kahn for National Research Initiatives. Knowbots are programmed by users to scan networks for various kinds of related information, regardless of the language or form in which it expressed. "Knowbots support parallel computations at different sites. They communicate with one another, and with various servers in the network and with users."

L

Langmuir-Blodgett

The name of a nanofabrication technique used to create ultrathin films (monolayers and isolated molecular layers), the end result of which is called a "Langmuir-Blodgett film". See Nanotechnology and Monolayers for more information.

LCD

(Liquid Crystal Display) is the predominant technology used in flat panel displays. The principle that makes the display work is this: A crystalís alignment can be altered with an electric current. If the crystal is lined up one way ñ it will allow the light waves to pass through a polarized filter, but if the electric current alters the crystalís alignment, it will guide light so that the polarized filter blocks the light. By densely packing red, blue and green light emitting crystals next to each other on a sheet (ícalled a substrateî), one can create a full color display. The great thing about LCD is that the crystals can be packed together closely, allowing for a higher-resolution, finer-detail display. The con is that LCDs are somewhat fragile, require a lot of power and are relatively less bright.

LEDs

(Light Emitting Diodes) work on a completely different concept. Traditionally LEDs are created from two semiconductors. By running current in one direction across the semiconductor the LED emits light of a particular frequency (hence a particular color) depending on the physical characteristics of the semiconductor used. The semiconductor is covered with a piece of plastic that focuses the light and increases the brightness. These semiconductors are very durable, there is no filament, they donít require much power, theyíre brighter and they last a long time. By densely packing red, blue and green LEDs next to each other on a substrate one can create a display.

The disadvantage of LEDs is that they are much larger ñ therefore the resolution is not nearly as good as LCD displays. Thatís why most LED displays are large, outdoor displays, not smaller devices, like monitors.

OLED or Organic LED is not made of semiconductors. Itís made from carbon-based molecules. That is the key science factor that leads to potentially eliminating LEDsí biggest drawback ñ size. The carbon-based molecules are much smaller. And according to a paper written by Dr. Uwe Hoffmann, Dr. Jutta Trube and Andreas Kl-ppel, entitled OLED - A bright new idea for flat panel displays ìOLED is brighter, thinner, lighter, and faster than the normal liquid crystal (LCD) display in use today. They also need less power to run, offer higher contrast, look just as bright from all viewing angles and are - potentially - a lot cheaper to produce than LCD screens.î LCD, LED, and OLED.

Ligand

In protein chemistry, a small molecule that is (or can be) bound by a larger molecule is termed a ligand. In organometallic chemistry, a moiety bonded to a central metal atom is also termed a ligand; the latter definition is more common in general chemistry.

Limited assembler

Assembler capable of making only certain products; faster, more efficient, and less liable to abuse than a general-purpose assembler.

Linde Scenario

A scenario for indefinite survival of intelligent life. It assumes it is possible to either create basement universes connected to the original universe with a wormhole or the existence of other cosmological domains. Intelligent life continually migrates to the new domains as the old grow too entropic to sustain life. [AS/Mitch Porter, 1997. The name refers to Linde's chaotic inflation cosmology, where new universes are continually spawned.]

Linear

Aside from its geometric meaning, linear describes systems in which an output is directly proportional to an input. In particular, a linear elastic system is one in which the internal displacements are (at equilibrium) directly proportional to applied forces.

Liposome

A type of nanoparticle made of lipids, or fat molecules, surrounding a water core. Liposomes, several of which are widely used to treat infectious diseases and cancer, were the first type of nanoparticle to be used to create therapeutic agents with novel characteristics.

LMNT

An abbreviation for *limited* molecular nanotechnology; a narrowly specified type of MNT, using only diamondoid reactions; much easier to achieve than general MNT, but with nearly equivalent appeal and impact.

Lofstrom Loop

An beanstalk-like megaconstruction based on a stream of magnetically accelerated bars linked together. The stream is sent into space, where a station rides it using magnetic hooks, redirects it horizontally to another station, which sends it downwards to a receiving station on the ground. From this station the stream is then sent back to the launch station (a purely vertical version is called a space fountain). This structure would contain a large amount of kinetic energy but could be built gradually and would only require enough energy to compensate for losses when finished. Elevators could be run along the streams, and geostationary installations could be placed along the horizontal top.

London dispersion force

An attractive force caused by quantum-mechanical electron correlation. For example, a neutral spherical molecule (such as a single argon atom) has no charge and produces no external electric field, yet a pair of molecules has a distribution of electron configurations weighted toward those with lesser electron-electron repulsions; this creates a small net attraction.

Lone pair

Two valence electrons of an atom that share an orbital but do not participate in a bond.

Low-dimension Structures

Quantum wells, quantum wire and quantum dots.

M

Machine-phase chemistry
The chemistry of systems in which all potentially reactive moieties follow controlled trajectories (e.g., guided by molecular machines working in vacuum).

Meat Machine
AKA Cabinet Beast. A box containing assemblers and raw material, within which is formed meat [or whatever else it was programmed to make].

Mechanical
Pertaining to the positions and motions of atoms, as defined by the positions of their nuclei; see electronic. A purely mechanical device can be described in terms of atomic positions and motions without reference to electronic properties, save through their effect on the potential energy function.

Macroscale
Larger than nanoscale; often implies a design that humans can directly interact with; too large to be built by a single assembler (one cubic micron of diamond contains 176 billion atoms).

Matter as Software
"Autonomous, motile microdevices clearly are on the horizon. They may be regarded as the first step in the evolution of a technology for "programming" the structure and properties

of material objects at the microscopic and the submicroscopic levels. As this evolution progresses, the physical and economic properties of such programmable matter are likely to become much like those of present day software."

Mechanochemistry

Chemistry accomplished by mechanical systems directly controlling the reactant molecules; the formation or breaking of chemical bonds under direct mechanical control. [See How does 'mechanochemistry' work?]
2. In this volume, the chemistry of processes in which mechanical systems operating with atomic-scale precision either guide, drive, or are driven by chemical transformations. In general usage, the chemistry of processes in which energy is converted from mechanical to chemical form, or vice versa.
3. Chemistry that deals with the conversion of chemical energy into mechanical work, or vice versa.
4. The direct, mechanical control of molecular structure formation and manipulation to form atomically precise products.

Mechanosynthesis

Chemical synthesis controlled by mechanical systems operating with atomic-scale precision, enabling direct positional selection of reaction sites; synthetic applications of mechanochemistry. Suitable mechanical systems include AFM mechanisms, molecular manipulators, and molecular mill systems. Processes that fall outside the intended scope of this definition include reactions guided by the incorporation of reactive moieties into a shared covalent framework (i.e., conventional intramolecular reactions), or by the binding of reagents to enzymes or enzymelike catalysts. (where) molecular tools with chemically specific tip structures can be used, sequentially, to modify a work piece and build a wide range of molecular structures.

Mechatronics

The study of the melding of AI and electromechanical machines to make machines that are greater than the sum of their parts.

Meme

An idea that replicates through a society as it is propagated through person-to-person interaction, both direct and indirect. Memetics is a field of study that focuses on memes' role in the evolution of a culture.

MEMS--MicroelectroMechanical Systems

Generic term to describe micron scale electrical/mechanical devices. See The beauty of MEMS: Simpler, more reliable, cheaper, and cool - Small Times for a great description and examples of use.

Mesoscale

A device or structure larger than the nanoscale (10^{-9} m) and smaller than the megascale; the exact size depends heavily on the context and usually ranges between very large nanodevices (10^{-7} m) and the human scale (1 m).

Metastable

A classical system is metastable if it is above its minimum-energy state, but requires an energy input before it can reach a lower-energy state; accordingly, a metastable system can act like a stable system, provided that energy inputs (e.g., thermal fluctuations) remain below some threshold. Systems with strong metastability are commonly described as stable. Quantum mechanical effects can permit metastable states to reach lower energies by tunneling, without an energy input; an associated, broader definition of metastable embraces all systems that have a long lifetime (by some standard) in a state above the minimum-energy state.

Micron

One millionth of a meter, or about 1/25,000 of an inch.

Microencapsulation

Individually encapsulated small particles. see Journal of Microencapsulation

Microfluidics

A multidisciplinary field comprising physics, chemistry,

engineering and biotechnology that studies the behavior of fluids at volumes thousands of times smaller than a common droplet. Microfluidic components form the basis of so-called "lab-on-a-chip" devices that can process microliter and nanoliter volumes and conduct highly sensitive analytical measurements. The fabrications techniques used to construct microfluidic devices are relatively inexpensive and are amenable both to highly elaborate, multiplexed devices and also to mass production. In a manner similar to that for microelectronics, microfluidic technologies enable the fabrication of highly integrated devices for performing several different functions on the same substrate chip. Microfluidics is a critical component in gene chip and protein chip development efforts.

Millimeter
One thousandth of a meter, or about 1/26 of an inch.

MIMIC
[micromoulding in capillaries] one-step rapid prototyping technique.

Misreaction
A chemical reaction that fails by yielding an unwanted product.

MM2
A molecular mechanics program developed by Norman Allinger and coworkers; the ``MM2 model'' is the molecular potential energy function described by the equations, rules, and parameters embodied in that program.

MM2/CSC
A molecular mechanics program developed by Cambridge Scientific Computing that closely follows the MM2 model, adding a graphical user interface and other features.

MNT
An abbreviation for molecular nanotechnology; refers to the concept of building complicated machines out of precisely designed molecules.

Modulus

Any of several measures of strain versus applied stress. See shear modulus, Young's modulus.

Moiety

A portion of a molecular structure having some property of interest.

Mole

A number of instances of something (typically a molecular species) equaling ~6.022 1023. Mole ordinarily means gram-mole; a kilogram-mole is ~6.022 1026.

Molecular Assembler

Also known as an assembler, a molecular assembler is a molecular machine that can build a molecular structure from its component building blocks.

Molecular Beam Epitaxy

[MBE] Process used to make compound (multi-layer) semiconductors. Consists of depositing alternating layers of materials, layer by layer, one type after another (such as the semiconductors gallium arsenide and aluminum gallium arsenide).

Molecular electronics

Any system with atomically precise electronic devices of nanometer dimensions, especially if made of discrete molecular parts rather than the continuous materials found in today's semiconductor devices.

Using molecule-based materials for electronics, sensing, and optoelectronics .... ME is the set of electronic behaviors in molecule-containing structures that are dependent upon the characteristic molecular organization of space .... ME behavior is fixed at the scale of the individual molecule, which is effectively the nanoscale.

Molecular Integrated Microsystems (MIMS)

Microsystems in which functions found in biological and nanoscale systems are combined with manufacturable materials.

Molecular machine

A mechanical device that performs a useful function using components of nanometer scale and defined molecular structure; includes both artificial nanomachines and naturally occurring devices found in biological systems.

Any machine with atomically precise parts of nanometer dimensions; can be used to describe molecular devices found in nature.

Molecular manipulator

A programmable device able to position molecular tools with high precision, for example, to direct a sequence of mechanosynthetic steps; a molecular assembler.

2. A device combining a proximal probe mechanism for atomically precise positioning with a molecule binding site on the tip; can serve as the basis for building complex structures by positional synthesis.

Molecular manufacturing

1. The building of complex structures by mechanochemical processes.

2. The production of complex structures via nonbiological mechanosynthesis (and subsequent assembly operations).

3. Manufacturing using molecular machinery, giving molecule-by-molecule control of products and by-products via positional chemical synthesis.

3. Manufacturing using molecular machinery, giving molecule-by-molecule control of products and by-products via positional chemical synthesis.

Exponential general-purpose molecular manufacturing -- that's a mouthful, but what does it mean? Let's take the phrase apart to see why it is so important. MANUFACTURING: The ability to make products, in this case ranging from clothing, to electronics, to medical devices, to books, to building materials, and much more. MOLECULAR manufacturing: The automated building of products from the bottom up, molecule by molecule, with atomic precision. This will make products that are extremely lightweight, flexible, durable, and potentially very 'smart'. GENERAL-PURPOSE molecular manufacturing: A manufacturing technology that will find many applications across many segments of society. Its extreme flexibility, precision, high capacity, and low cost will cause rapid adoption almost everywhere, and therefore will have disruptive effects in many industries. EXPONENTIAL general-purpose molecular manufacturing: The word exponential refers to the rapid pace -- probably unprecedented -- at which this technology may be deployed. A compact automated molecular manufacturing system will be able to make more manufacturing systems. We're talking about factories that can build duplicate factories -- and probably do it in less than a single day. The math is simple: if one factory makes two, and two factories make four, then within ten days you could have one thousand factories, in ten more days a million factories, and ten days after that a billion factories. Within the span of just a few weeks, in theory, every household in the world could have one of their own, to make most of the products they need, at just the cost of raw materials. Exponential general-purpose molecular manufacturing means a manufacturing system capable of making a wide range of technologically advanced products, far superior to what we have today, much cheaper, much faster, and able to multiply its own source of production exponentially. From Responsible Nanotechnology.

Molecular mechanics models
Many of the properties of molecular systems are determined by the molecular potential energy function. Molecular mechanics models approximate this function as a sum of 2-atom, 3-atom, and 4-atom terms, each determined by the geometries and bonds of the component atoms. The 2-atom and 3-atom terms describing bonded interactions roughly correspond to linear springs.

Molecular medicine
A variety of pharmaceutical techniques and therapies in use today.
2. Studying molecules as they relate to health and disease, and manipulating those molecules to improve the diagnosis, prevention, and treatment of disease.

Molecular mill

A mechanochemical processing system characterized by limited motions and repetitive operations without programmable flexibility (see molecular manipulator).

Molecular nanotechnology (MNT)

The ability to construct shapes, devices, and machines with atomic precision, and to combine them into a wide range of products inexpensively.

2. Thorough, inexpensive control of the structure of matter based on molecule-by-molecule control of products and byproducts; the products and processes of molecular manufacturing, including molecular machinery.

See nanotechnology.

Molecular recognition

A chemical term referring to processes in which molecules adhere in a highly specific way, forming a larger structure; an enabling technology for nanotechnology.

Molecular surgery or molecular repair

Analysis and physical correction of molecular structures in the body using medical nanomachines.

Molecular systems engineering

Design, analysis, and construction of systems of molecular parts working together to carry out a useful purpose.

Molecule

Group of atoms held together by chemical bonds; the typical unit manipulated by nanotechnology.

2. A set of atoms linked by covalent bonds. A macroscopic piece of diamond is technically a single molecule. (Sets of atoms linked by bonds of other kinds are sometimes also termed molecules.)

Molecular manufacturing

Production using molecular machinery, giving molecule-by-molecule control of products and by-products via positional chemical synthesis. Molecular manufacturing promises to be more efficient than traditional manufacturing, resulting in better quality products, by assembling products directly from the smallest pieces: Atoms and molecules.

Molecular Wire
A molecular wire - the simplest electronic component - is a quasi-one-dimensional molecule that can transport charge carriers (electrons or holes) between its ends.

Monomer
The units from which a polymer is constructed.

Monomolecular Computing
The implantation inside a single molecule of ALL the functional groups or circuits to realize a calculation, without any help from external artifices such as re-configuration, calculation sharing between the user and the machine, or selection of the operational devices.

Moore's Law
Coined in 1965 by Gordon Moore, future chairman and chief executive of Intel, it stated at the time that the of number transistors packed into an integrated circuit had doubled every year since the technology's inception four years earlier. In 1975 he revised this to every two years, and most people quote 18 months. The trend cannot continue indefinitely with current lithographic techniques, and a limit is seen in ten to fifteen years. However, the baton could be passed to nanoelectronics, to continue the trend (though the smoothness of the curve will very likely be disrupted if a completely new technology is introduced).

Nanarchist
Someone who circumvents government control to use nanotechnology, or someone who advocates this.

Nanarchy
The use of automatic law-enforcement by nanomachines or robots, without any human control.

Nanite
Machines with atomic-scale components. (Popularized by the Star Trek episode "Evolution") As to their weight, a popular question: "Do you 'feel' heavier after you drink a mouthful of water? A mouthful of water, roughly 5 cm^3, would have the same mass as a ~2 terabot (2 trillion nanites) dose of 1 micron^3 nanorobots. You'll never feel it." Robert A. Freitas Jr. "Nanobot" and "Nanorobot" usually mean the same thing.

Nano-
A prefix meaning one billionth (1/1,000,000,000).
2. A prefix meaning one-billionth. It comes from the Greek word nanos ("dwarf").

Nanoarray
An ultra-sensitve, ultra-miniaturized array for biomolecular analysis. BioForce Nanosciences' Nanoarrays utilize approximately 1/10,000th of the surface area occupied by a

conventional microarray, and over 1,500 nanoarray spots can be placed in the area occupied by a single microarray domain.

Nanoassembler

The Holy Grail of nanotechnology; once a perfected nanoassembler is availble, building anything becomes possible, with physics and the imagination the only limitation (of course each item would have to be designed first, which is another small hurdle). See Bootstrapping a Nanofactory "So how hard is it to build a nanofactory? You need to start with a working fabricator, a nanoscale device that can combine individual molecules into useful shapes. But once you have that, the rest is pretty straightforward."

Nanobalance

Simply put, a nanoscale balance for determining mass, small enough to weigh viruses and other sub-micron scale particles. "A mass attached at the end of a nanotube shifts its resonance frequency. If the nanotube is calibrated (i.e., its spring constant known), it is possible to measure the mass of the attached particle." A nanobalance "could be useful for determining the mass of other objects on the femtogram to picogram size range."

Nanobarcode

SurroMed's Nanobarcode™ technology uses cylindrically-shaped colloidal metal nanoparticles, in which the metal composition can be alternated along the length and the size of each metal segment can be controlled. Intrinsic differences in reflectivity between the metal segments allow individual particles to be identified by conventional optical microscopy.

Nanobeads

Polymer beads with diameters of between 0.1 to 10 micrometers. Also called nanodots, nanocrystals and quantum beads. Impregnating fluorescent crystal chips into these beads allows simultaneous measurement of thousands of biological interactions, a stepping stone for breakthroughs in the diagnosis and treatment of disease. ... with the potential to accelerate drug discovery and clinical diagnostics."

Nanobiotechnology

Applying the tools and processes of MNT to build devices for studying biosystems, in order to learn from biology how to create better nanoscale devices. Should hasten the creation of useful micro devices that mimic living biological systems.

Nanobot

see Nanite

Nanobubbles

Tiny air bubbles on colloid surfaces. Thought to reduce drag, such as would be of benefit to swimmers wearing a suit coverd in them.

Nanocantilever

The simplest micro-electro-mechanical system (MEMS) that can be easily machined and mass-produced via the same techniques used to make computer chips. The ability to detect extremely small displacements make nanocantilever beams an ideal device for detecting extremely small forces, stresses and masses. Nanocantilevers coated with antibodies, for example, will bend from the mass added when substrate binds to its antibody, providing a detector capable of sensing the presence of single molecules of clinical importance.

Nanochemical

Refers to chemistry accomplished by mechanical systems directly controlling reactant molecules-the formation or breaking of chemical bonds under direct mechanical control.

Nanochemistry

The study of the synthesis and characterization of materials in the nanoscale size range (1 to 10 nanometers). These materials include large organic molecules, inorganic cluster compounds, and metallic or semiconductor particles. The synthesis of inorganic materials of nanometer dimension is important because the small size of these particles endows them with unusual structural and optical properties that may find application in catalysis and electrooptical devices. Moreover, such materials may be valuable as precursor phases to strong ceramics. Approaches to the synthesis of these materials have focused on constraining the reaction environment through the use of surface-bound organic additives, porous glasses, zeolites, clays, or polymers. The use of synthetic approaches that are inspired by the biological processes result in the deposition of inorganic materials such as bones, shells, and teeth (biomineralization). This biomimetic approach involves the use of assemblies of biological molecules that provide nanoscale reaction environments in which inorganic materials can be prepared in an organized and controlled manner. Examples of biological assemblies include phospholipid vesicles and the polypeptide micelle of the iron storage protein, ferritin.

Vesicles are bounded by an organic membrane that provides a spatial limit on the size of the reaction volume. If a chemical reaction is undertaken in this confined space that leads to the formation of an inorganic material, the size of the product will also be constrained to the dimensions of the organic host structure. This can be considered as analogous to producing inorganic materials in a soap bubble, except that the soap bubble is very, very small. Provided that the chemical and physical conditions are not too severe to disrupt the organic membrane, these supramolecular assemblies may have advantages over inorganic hosts such as clays and zeolites because the chemical nature of the organic surface can be systematically modified so that controlled reactions can be accomplished.

Surfactant vesicles have been employed in a number of studies involving semiconductor, catalytic, and magnetic materials (see table). In the general method for preparing these materials, vesicles are formed spontaneously by sonicating aqueous solutions of phospholipids (Fig. 1). The presence of metal ions in the solution results in their encapsulation within the 25—50-nm internal volume of the enclosed aqueous space of the vesicle. The vesicle membrane is a bilayer of 4.5 nm thickness, and it prevents leakage of the metal ions back into the bulk solution. Thus, if metal ions are now exchanged from the bulk solution for inert cations such as the sodium ion (Na^+; by ion-exchange chromatography), the remaining entrapped ions can be subjected to chemical reactions solely within the intravesicular volume. The simplest procedure is to add a membrane-permeable coreactant such as gaseous hydrogen sulfide (H_2S). The H_2S rapidly diffuses through the phospholipid membrane and combines with the encapsulated metal ions to give an insoluble metal sulfide precipitate. As the number of entrapped metal ions is usually less than 10,000, semiconductor particles in the nanometer size range can be routinely produced. An extension of this method, in which an increase in the pH of the bulk solution provides an excess of hydroxide ions (OH^-) that slowly diffuse through the surfactant membrane, results in the formation of metal oxide particles. In particular, nanophase iron oxides with catalytic and magnetic properties have been synthesized.

The presence of the surfactant membrane in these nanoscale chemical reactions can have a profound effect on the structure and properties of the resulting inorganic materials. For example, the particles cannot come into direct contact, and the vesicles are usually charged; thus there is negligible aggregation or macroscopic precipitation. Under certain circumstances, the product is stable over many weeks as a monodisperse sol of finely divided particles.

Biomimetic approaches in the nanoscale synthes is and endline; of inorganic materials

System	Materials
Vesicles	Pt, Ag
	Cadmium sulfide (CdS), zinc sulfide (ZnS), silver sulfide (Ag_2S), cobalt sulfide (CoS)
	Silver oxide (Ag_2O)
	Iron oxyhydroxide (FeO·OH),
	Magnetite (Fe_3O_4)
	Aluminum oxide (Al_2O_3)
	Calcium phosphates
Ferritin	Iron(III) sulfide (FeS)
	Manganese oxyhydroxide (MnO·OH)
	Uranium trioxide (UO_3)
	Magnetite (Fe_3O_4)

Fig. 1 Nanoscale synthesis of inorganic metal oxides by means of surfactant phospholipid vesicles. Cations (M^+) are encapsulated by sonication and replaced in the bulk solution by inert cations (P^+). Slow diffusion of hydroxide ions (OH^-) through the organic membrane results in intravesicular precipitation of metal oxides.

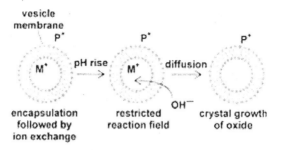

One problem encountered with the use of phospholipid vesicles is their sensitivity to changes in temperature and ionic strength. Procedures have been developed in which the biomolecular cage of the iron storage protein, ferritin, has been used as a nanoscale reaction environment for the synthesis of inorganic materials (see table). Ferritin is a robust molecule constructed from 24 polypeptide subunits arranged into a hollow sphere of 8—9-nm internal diameter. The native protein contains a 5-nm-diameter core of a hydrated iron(III) oxide (ferrihydrite) within the internal cavity. Hydrophilic and hydrophobic channels penetrate the protein shell and provide the means by which iron atoms can be accumulated within or removed from the protein cavity. In the laboratory vessel, the iron can be readily removed by reductive dissolution to give intact empty protein cages (apoferritin).

Several approaches utilize ferritin in the production of inorganic nanoscale particles (Fig. 2). In the simplest approach the native iron oxide core is transformed into another material by chemical reaction within the protein shell. For example, exposure of the red-brown protein solution to H_2S results in a green coloration due to the formation of amorphous iron(III) sulfide (FeS) cores, approximately 7.5 nm in diameter. No precipitation is observed because the FeS particles remain encapsulated within the protein shell.

Fig. 2 Use of the supramolecular protein cage of ferritin in the
synthesis of nanophase inorganic materials.

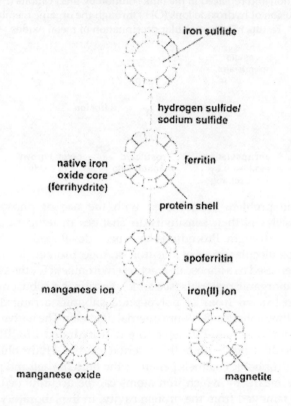

Alternatively, the native iron oxide cores can be removed
from their protein shells by the use of appropriate reducing
and chelating agents. The resulting empty apoferritin
molecules are structurally intact, and can be readily
reconstituted at room temperature and pH 7 by incubation
of the protein in aerated Fe(II)-containing solutions. Moreover,
other metal oxides can be formed within the protein cavity.
For example, incubation of the empty protein cages with
aqueous Fe(II) but at a pH of 8.5 and temperature of 65°C
(149°F) results in the synthesis of nanometer-size magnetic
iron oxides such as magnetite (Fe_3O_4) and maghemite (γ-

Fe_2O_3) [Fig. 2]. The resulting protein, termed magnetoferritin, is magnetic. Other metals oxides, such as manganese oxyhydroxide ($MnO·OH$) and hydrated uranium trioxide (UO_3), can be synthesized within the protein cavity by incubation of apoferritin with the appropriate metal salt solutions in the presence of air.

Nanochondria

Nanomachines existing inside living cells, participating in their biochemistry (like mitochondria) and/or assembling various structures.

Nanocomputer

A computer made from components (mechanical, electronic, or otherwise) built at the nanometer scale. These computers could be many orders-of-magnitude faster than today's, which enables software to take proportional leaps.

Nanochips

We are approaching the limits of standard microchip technology; thus, the "nanochip" -- a next-smaller microchip. [ed] They are also a next-gen device for mass storage, of significantly higher density, with greater speed, and much lower cost.

Nanocomposite

A material that is stiffer and lighter than traditional thermoplastics, and less brittle in cold temperatures. Nanocomposites are made by introducing a solid material into a plastic resin to give it added strength. Because there is less additive material, they are more recyclable than olefins and other thermoplastics.

Nanocones

Nonplanar graphitic structures. Carbon-based structures with five-fold symmetry that form due to disclination defects in two-dimensional graphene sheets. They have been observed as nanotube caps and as freestanding structures.

Nanocontainers

"Micellar nanocontainers" or "Micelles," these are nanoscale polymeric containers that could be used to selectively deliver hydrophobic drugs to specific sites within individual cells. See Nanocontainers deliver on drugs.

Nanocrystals

Also known as nanoscale semiconductor crystals. "Nanocrystals are aggregates of anywhere from a few hundred to tens of thousands of atoms that combine into a crystalline form of matter known as a "cluster." Typically around ten nanometers in diameter, nanocrystals are larger than molecules but smaller than bulk solids and therefore frequently exhibit physical and chemical properties somewhere in between. Given that a nanocrystal is virtually all surface and no interior, its properties can vary considerably as the crystal grows in size."

"Nanocrystals might be used to make super-strong and long-lasting metal parts. The crystals also might be added to plastics and other metals to make new types of composite structures for everything from cars to electronics." See Discovery could bring widespread uses for 'nanocrystals'. Single atoms caged inside nanocrystals gives you a "quantum confined atom", or QCA, "with potential uses ranging from clear-glass sunglasses to bio-sensors to optical computing and just about anything optical in between." See Nanocrystals Technology Shines New Light on Optics, A Good Look at Nanocrystals, and Researchers Turn Scrap to Strength with Nanocrystals.

Nano Cubic Technology

An ultra-thin layer coating that results in higher resolution for recording digital data, ultra-low noise and high signal-to-noise ratios that are ideal for magneto-resistive (MR) heads. It is capable of catapulting data cartridge and digital videotape to one-terabyte native (uncompressed) capacities and floppy disk capacities to three gigabytes.

Nanodefenses

Any of the "good" goo's, such a Blue Goo. Protectors against Grey Goo, destructive nanoswarms, and the like.

Nanodisaster

See the various 'goo' scenerios that have potentially negative outcomes.

Nanoelectronics

Electronics on a nanometer scale, whether made by current techniques or nanotechnology; includes both molecular electronics and nanoscale devices resembling today's semiconductor devices.

2. Developments in integrated circuits and storage devices used in computers have proceeded at an exponential rate: at present it takes 2-3 years for each successive halving of the component size. Information storage has followed a similar trend in miniaturization of the size of the bits of magnetized material used in hard disks. However, these technologies have fundamental limits, below which the devices no longer function in a predictable manner. For instance, the oxide layers used in complementary metal oxide semiconductor (CMOS) devices are becoming so thin that they conduct electricity in a quantum-mechanical manner by electron tunneling. In 1998 it was estimated that microelectronics and magnetic storage technologies would reach their ultimate limits within 10-30 years. Projections for very large scale integration (VLSI) predict that a single chip will accommodate 90 million transistors with a feature size of 70 nanometers and a clock speed of 900 MHz by the year 2010. Currently, many critical dimensions in semiconductor devices are in the 100-nm range, with some insulating layers being tens of nanometers thick.

There is intensive effort to drive miniaturization even further. Miniaturization all the way down to the level of individual atoms and molecules would enable the fabrication of highly dense, fast, and energy-efficient devices. Energy dissipation in current devices can approach 100 W. As devices become more dense, the electronic elements must be designed to be more efficient. Another potential advantage of using individual molecules is that electronic circuitry could be prefabricated using chemical synthesis. This approach would permit techniques such as self-assembly to be used in fabrication, whereby molecules diffuse and dock onto specific connections.

The term nanoelectronics refers to electronic devices in which dimensions are in the range of atoms up to 100 nm. Nanoelectronics is regarded as the successor to microelectronics because it is capable of extending miniaturization further toward the ultimate limit of individual atoms and molecules. The first applications will probably be in the military sector.

The implementation schemes and device architectures for nanoelectronics may involve conceptually different approaches to future computational devices, such as DNA (deoxyribonucleic acid) computing and quantum computing, where atoms could act as quantum logic gates. Both of these concepts rely on controlling individual atoms or molecules, and may also be regarded as being in the realm of nanoelectronics.

Currently there are no established mass-production techniques for commercial nanoelectronic devices, nor has a well-defined fabrication strategy that can be scaled for massive integration of components been established. Whereas for microelectronic devices the transistor forms a basic building block, it is not clear what the basic (three-terminal) element of a nanoelectronic device will be. Likewise, a well-defined architecture, required to process data, has yet to be established. Nanoelectronics research is currently looking not only for the successor to CMOS processing but also for a replacement for the transistor itself. On the scale of 10-nm dimensions, components have a wavelength comparable to that of an electron at the Fermi energy. The confinement and coherence of the electron gives rise to gross deviations from the classical charge transport found in conventional devices. Quantum-mechanical laws become increasingly dominant on the nanoscale, and it is probable that nanoelectronics will operate on quantum principles.

One popular approach has been to use small conducting islands in which electrons are confined and quantized in a definite state. These islands are typically connected to electrodes by thin tunneling barriers. Quantum dots, resonant tunnel devices, and single-electron transistors are examples of devices that use this basic concept, albeit in different ways. Single-electron transistors are an example of a three-terminal device in which the charge of a single electron is sufficient to switch the source-to-drain current. The tiny energy required to drive single-electron transistor devices makes this approach very appealing. Nevertheless, a variety of drawbacks and obstacles limit the application of such devices in solid-state nanoelectronics, for example, their sensitivity to small fluctuations in voltage and background charges, which tend to accumulate in semiconductors. Such problems suggest that single-electron devices may be used for storage rather than logic functions. Currently, such devices operate at cryogenic temperatures, although there are a few examples of room temperature operation.

Owing to the dimensions in which nanoelectronics operates, there are two possible approaches to the fabrication of nanoelectronic devices: top down and bottom up (Fig. 1).

Top-down is the extension of established methods of engineering and microelectronics processing that relies on a patterning process often described in terms of depositing, patterning, and etching layers of material to define the circuitry and active elements. Top-down approaches rely on control of damage, and as the structures become smaller the defects make device operation increasingly problematic. Moreover, as these technologies are pushed to smaller sizes, the cost increases drastically, tolerances become more difficult to maintain, and the engineering laws of scaling become inapplicable. To scale such technologies to the atomic and molecular level, the use of softer methods with atomic tolerances based on bottom-up approaches will eventually become mandatory.

Present top-down fabrication is limited by the wavelength of the light used in the photolithography process, which illuminates proximity masks containing the pattern to be transferred to the substrate. To overcome this limit, shorter wavelengths are required, such as in extreme ultraviolet lithography. X-ray lithography is currently the leading technology in the drive to replace photolithography as a large-scale production tool because it uses masks, which are suited to high-volume production. Major challenges are mask fabrication and placement accuracy. Electron-beam lithography uses a finely focused beam of high-energy electrons to define a pattern. However, because the beam must be scanned to define the pattern, the technique in its present form is considered too slow for anything but the production of masks. Proposals to employ arrays of miniaturized electron guns are under investigation to alleviate this problem.

Fig. 1 Developments in solid-state technology and chemistry. Miniaturization in technology is based on ever-smaller and simpler components. Macromolecular chemistry involves a bottom-up approach, in which units of atoms are connected to form structures of ever-increasing complexity. Understanding and control of biology is also approaching the scale of individual atoms and molecules (for example, in drug design), and so converges with chemistry and microelectronics. Concepts in all three fields may be used in the design, fabrication, and operational principles of nanoelectronic devices.

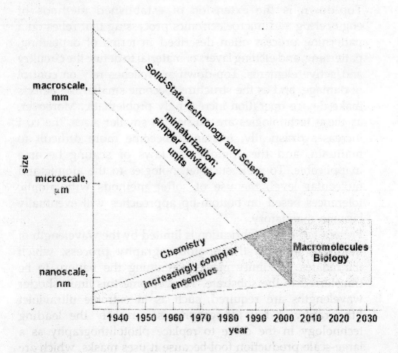

This term describes device fabrication on an atom-by-atom basis. Molecules, which are prefabricated arrangements of atoms in a functional form, are also appealing for bottom-up fabrication. The advantage of the bottom-up approach lies in the design and chemical synthesis of functional molecules by the billions, which can then be assembled into nanoelectronic devices. The assembly of these perfect molecular units is more problematic, but two principal methods for engineering atoms and molecules currently exist.

One approach involves self-assembly, whereby specific intermolecular forces allow molecules to arrange themselves into more complex structures. Supramolecular chemistry is the art of designing molecules that arrange themselves into functional entities held together by intermolecular forces. Success has also been achieved in patterning surfaces using elastomeric stamps containing self-assembling molecules that transfer themselves to a surface upon contact.

The development of the scanning tunneling microscope and related scanning probe microscopy tools such as the scanning force microscope provide another approach to bottom-up fabrication. In scanning tunneling microscopy, a sharp tip, a needle of conical shape typically terminating in a single atom, is used to reposition, chemically change, or deposit individual atoms. It is an extension of mechanical assembly techniques on the atomic scale. Scanning tunneling microscopy is the highest-resolution member of the family of scanning probe microscopy techniques, which all use sharp tips in different modes of operation. A major drawback of scanning probe microscopy is that it is a serial process. To overcome this, a system employing 1000 scanning tips has been realized using micromechanics. It is anticipated that several thousand tips working in unison can be fabricated. These small devices also allow patterning to be conducted at higher speeds because of the higher mechanical frequencies of the components.

Clear evidence that scanning probe microscopy techniques are an ultimate engineering tool has been provided by demonstrations of the ability to finely control and assemble individual atoms at low temperatures, around -270°C (-454°F). The low temperature is necessary to keep the atoms from becoming thermally agitated and diffusing away. This capability has also been extended to room temperature in experiments in which molecules were repositioned on surfaces.

An abacus with individual molecules as beads having a diameter of less than 1 nm has been constructed. The "finger" to move these beads is the ultrafine tungsten tip of a scanning tunneling microscope, which also renders the result of such a "calculation" visible when operated in imaging mode. Stable rows of ten C_{60} (buckminsterfullerene) molecules were formed along steps just one atom high on a copper surface. These steps act as "rails," similar to the earliest form of the abacus, which had grooves instead of rods to keep the beads in line. Individual molecules were then approached by the scanning tunneling microscope tip and pushed back and forth in a precisely controlled way to count from 0 to 10 (Fig. 2). This work is a further step in bottom-up fabrication. It points the way to the assembly of more complex structures molecule by molecule, as nature does, and thus breaks ground for entirely new fabrication technologies in nanoelectronics.

Fig. 2 Abacus with individual molecules that are moved by the tip of a scanning tunneling microscope (STM). (a) Repositioning of a C_{60} molecule adsorbed on Cu(111) step sites along the step direction.

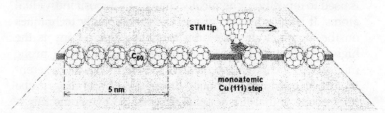

In an extension of electrical transport studies of C_{60} molecules that involved electrically contacting individual molecules, an experimental electronic device with a tiny active part was demonstrated. It consists of a single C_{60} molecule, also known as a bucky ball, actuated by the ultrasharp tip of a scanning tunneling microscope, and represents a fully functional electromechanical amplifier. Applying a mechanical force to a single bucky ball using a scanning tunneling microscope tip can change its electrical conductance continuously and reversibly. By gently squeezing the bucky ball by lowering the tip only one-tenth of a nanometer, the molecular structure is deformed slightly, which in turn changes its electrical

Fig. 3 Effects of compressing the cage of a C_{60} molecule with the tip apex of a scanning tunneling microscope (STM). (a) Compression of 0.1 nm, producing a two-order-of-magnitude increase in the current intensity through the molecule. (b) Comparison of conductance spectra of compressed and uncompressed molecules, showing how external deformation causes broadening and shifting of the highest occupied and lowest unoccupied molecular orbital (HOMO and LUMO) levels. The vertical band indicates the path of the tunneling electrons from the Fermi level of the tip.

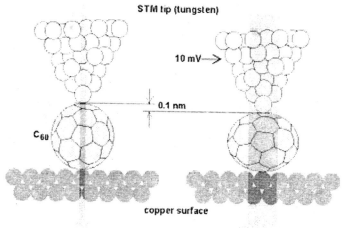

STM tip (tungsten)

10 mV

0.1 nm

C_{60}

copper surface

current

(a)

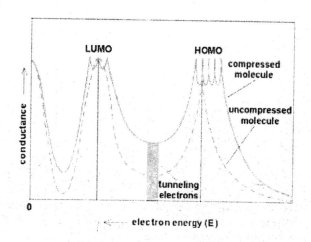

LUMO   HOMO

compressed molecule

uncompressed molecule

conductance

tunneling electrons

0

electron energy (E)

(b)

properties. The resistance of the squeezed bucky ball is 100 times lower than that of the uncompressed molecule, which allows electrons to tunnel more easily through the molecule. A small voltage (10 mV) applied to a piezoelectric element of the tip to squeeze the molecule results in a fivefold voltage gain in the device (Fig. 3).

By externally deforming the molecule, the highest occupied and lowest unoccupied molecular orbital (HOMO and LUMO) levels (which are the equivalent of the valence and conduction bands in a conventional semiconductor) are broadened and shifted (Fig. 3b). This effect increases the weight of the tails of those levels at the electrode's Fermi level and therefore accounts for the increased conductance (transparency) of the molecule. (Electron transport at small bias voltage is still linear with voltage in this region.) One interesting consequence of the molecule's compression is that normally degenerate molecular levels (such as the fivefold HOMO and the threefold LUMO of a C_{60} molecule) are split in energy, which explains the five and three peaks of these orbitals that appear on the conductance spectrum under compression.

The next step in further decreasing the size of the device is to replace the macroscopic piezo-actuated electromechanical gate (the scanning tunneling microscope tip) with a smaller component. A micromechanical electrode actuated by electrostatic, thermomechanical, or other means might be used to vary the pressure on a molecule, thereby reducing the overall dimensions of the complete amplifier.

In another approach, researchers fabricated a transistor using nanotubes. Carbon nanotubes are molecularly perfect tubes with nanometer-scale diameters formed from carbon atoms. They are electrical conductors and have attracted much attention as candidates for molecular computers. Currently, carbon nanotubes are limited in their application to nanoelectronics by their variety of forms and types. They lack the uniformity of molecules synthesized by conventional chemical techniques, which can be purified to trillions of exactly identical copies. However, their good electrical characteristics do make them attractive candidates for nanoelectronics. Much research is being conducted to further develop methods to fabricate better tubes in larger quantities.

The first atomic switch consisted of a xenon atom that was switched back and forth between a scanning tunneling microscope tip and a surface at low temperature. Associated with the motion of the atom was a change in the electric current flowing in the junction. This approach to the ultimate miniaturization of electronic components encouraged researchers to propose a number of devices.

In a simulated atomic relay based on this principle, a single atom in an atomic wire was switched in and out of registry by a third electrode, also made of an atomic wire. An atomic wire consists of single atoms lined up in a row. Such structures have been created in the laboratory using, for example, a surface with atomic grooves. A cheap and reliable method to fabricate massive arrays of such wires just where they are needed is the focus of much research. A molecular relay based on similar concepts but with a differently shaped molecule has been proposed.

Molecular switches and other types of devices have been chemically synthesized from molecules that are mechanically interlinked. Although such devices are appealing in terms of their size, the fabrication of a reliable switch represents a major challenge in the quest for molecular-scale computers.

Nanofabrication

The practice of sculpting or building, with man-made tools, products, structures and processes with atomic precision.
2. Construction of items using assemblers and stock molecules. see Nanofacture. AKA: nanoscale engineering.

Nanofactory

A self-contained macroscale manufacturing system, consisting of many molecular manufacturing systems feeding a convergent assembly system.

Nanofacture

The fabrication of goods using nanotechnology [Geoff Dale 1995]. see Nanofabrication.

Nanofilters

One opportunity for nanoscale filters is for the separation of molecules, such as proteins or DNA, for research in genomics.

See Selective nanofilters for proteins, DNA Another, as "masks to prevent exposure to biological pathogens such as viruses that can be as small as 30 nanometers in diameter." See Biologically inspired nanotechnology. And another use is in water filtration.

Nanofluidics
Controlling nano-scale amounts of fluids.

Nanogate
A device that precisely meters the flow of tiny amounts of fluid. Precise control of the flow restriction is accomplished by deflecting a highly polished cantilevered plate. The opening is adjustable on a sub-nanometer scale, limited by the roughness of the polished plates. Thus, the Nanogate is an Ultra Surface Finish Effect Mechanism (USFEM). The Nanogate can be fabricated on a macro-, meso- or micro- (MEMs) scale. See Nanogate: A Fundamental New Device for Nanofluidics Nanoguitar: "Made for fun to illustrate the technology -- the world's smallest guitar is 10 micrometers long -- about the size of a single cell -- with six strings each about 50 nanometers, or 100 atoms, wide. Just one of several structures that Cornell researchers believe are the world's smallest silicon mechanical devices. Researchers made these devices at the Cornell Nanofabrication Facility, bringing microelectromechanical devices, or MEMS, to a new, even smaller scale -- the nano-sized world." See World's smallest silicon mechanical devices are made at Cornell.

Nanogypsy
Someone who travels form place to place, spreading the "nano" word. Usually a person who takes the most optimistic viewpoint, and is enthusitic.

Nanohacking
Describes what MNT is all about -- "hacking" at the molecular level.

Nanohorns
One of the SWNT (single walled carbon nanotube) types, with an irregular horn-like shape, which may be a critical component

of a new generation of fuel cells. "The main characteristic of the carbon nanohorns is that when many of the nanohorns group together an aggregate (a secondary particle) of about 100 nanometers is created. The advantage being, that when used as an electrode for a fuel cell, not only is the surface area extremely large, but also, it is easy for the gas and liquid to permeate to the inside. In addition, compared with normal nanotubes, because the nanohorns are easily prepared with high purity it is expected to become a low-cost raw material." See NEC uses Carbon Nanotubes to Develop a Tiny Fuel Cell for Mobile Applications and here is a TEM image.

Nanoimprinting

Sometimes called soft lithography. A technique that is very simple in concept, and totally analogous to traditional mould- or form-based printing technology, but that uses moulds (masters) with nanoscale features. As with the printing press, the potential for mass production is clear. There are two forms of nanoimprinting, one that uses pressure to make indentations in the form of the mould on a surface, the other, more akin to the printing press, that relies on the application of "ink" applied to the mould to stamp a pattern on a surface. Other techniques such as etching may then follow.

Nanoimprint Machine

A form of soft lithography.

Nanoindentation

Nanoindentation is similar to conventional hardness testing performed on a much smaller scale. The force required to press a sharp diamond indenter into a material is measured as a function of indentation depth. As depth resolution is on the scale of nanometers (hence the name of the instrument), it is possible to conduct indentation experiments even on thin films. Two quantities which can be readily extracted from nanoindentation experiments are the material's modulus, or stiffness, and its hardness, which can be correlated to yield strength. Investegators have also used nanoindentation to study creep, plastic flow, and fracture of materials.

Nanolithography

Writing on the nanoscale. From the Greek words Nanos - Dwarf, Lithos - rock, and grapho - to write, this word literally means "small writing on rocks."

There are many different types of Nanoimprint Lithography, but two of them are most important: Thermoplastic Nanoimprint lithography and Step and Flash Nanoimprint Lithography.

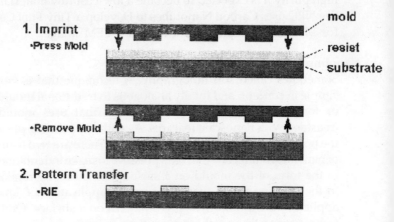

schematic of thermoplastic nanoimprint lithography

Thermoplastic Nanoimprint lithography (T-NIL) is the earliest and most mature nanoimprint lithography developed by Professor Stephen Y. Chou's group. In a standard T-NIL process, a thin layer of imprint resist (thermal plastic polymer) is spun coated onto the sample substrate. Then the mold, which has pre-defined topological patterns, is brought into contact with the sample and pressed again each other under certain pressure. When heated up above the glass transition temperature of the polymer, the pattern on the mold is pressed into the melt polymer film. After being cooled down, the mold is separated from the sample and the pattern resist is left on the substrate. A pattern transfer process (Reactive Ion Etching, normally) can be used to transfer the pattern in the resist to the underneath substrate.

Schematic of Step and Flash Nanoimprint Lithography

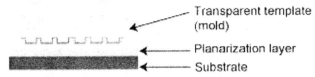

- Transparent template (mold)
- Planarization layer
- Substrate

Step 1: Orient template and substrate

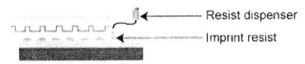

- Resist dispenser
- Imprint resist

Step 2: Dispense drops of liquid imprint resist

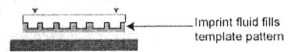

- Imprint fluid fills template pattern

Step 3: Lower template and fill pattern

Schematic of Step and Flash Nanoimprint Lithography

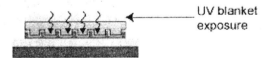

- UV blanket exposure

Step 4: Polymerize imprint fluid with UV exposure

- Exact replica of template pattern

Step 5: Separate template from substrate

Thermoplastic Nanoimprint lithography (T-NIL) is the earliest and most mature nanoimprint lithography developed by Professor Stephen Y. Chou's group. In a standard T-NIL process, a thin layer of imprint resist (thermal plastic polymer) is spun coated onto the sample substrate. Then the mold, which has pre-defined topological patterns, is brought into contact with the sample and pressed again each other under certain pressure. When heated up above the glass transition temperature of the polymer, the pattern on the mold is pressed into the melt polymer film. After being cooled down, the.mold is separated from the sample and the pattern resist is left on the substrate. A pattern transfer process (Reactive Ion Etching, normally) can be used to transfer the pattern in the resist to the underneath substrate.

Step and Flash Imprint Lithography (SFIL) is develop by Prof. Grant Willson's group. In SFIL, a UV curable liquid resist is apply to the sample substrate and the mold is mormally made of transparent material like fused silica. After the mold and the substrate are pressed together, a UV light is shined and the resist is cured and becomes solid. After mold separation, similar pattern transfer process can be used to tranfer the pattern in resist onto the underneath material.

Nanomachine

An artificial eutactic mechanical device that relies on nanometer-scale components; see molecular machine.

2. An artificial molecular machine of the sort made by molecular manufacturing.

3. An artificial molecular machine of the sort made by molecular manufacturing.

Nanomachining

Like traditional machining, where portions of the structure are removed or modified, nanomachining involves changing the structure of nano-scale materials or molecules.

Nanomanipulation

The process of building things from the bottom up, atom by atom. Nanomanipulation can be classified into two categories: Nanofabrication and self-assembly.

2. Uses virtual reality (VR) goggles and a force feedback probe as an interface to a scanning probe microscope, providing researchers with a new way to interact with the atomic world. Researchers can travel over genes, tickle viruses, push bacteria around, and tap on molecules - the nanoManipulator simplifies the process and allows researchers to play with their atoms. University of North Carolina at Chapel Hill (UNC-CH) The Nanomanipulator from the Center for Computer Integrated Systems for Microscopy and Manipulation (CISMM) at UNC Chapel Hill. Part of the Nanoscale Science Research Group (NSRG).

3. The process of manipulating items at an atomic or molecular scale in order to produce precise structures.

Nanomaterials

Can be subdivided into nanoparticles, nanofilms and nanocomposites. The focus of nanomaterials is a bottom up approach to structures and functional effects whereby the building blocks of materials are designed and assembled in controlled ways.

Nanomechanical

Being mechanical and very small; for example, a robot that can manipulate single molecules.
Pertaining to nanomachines.

2. Refers to a small, mechanical device, such as a robot, that can manipulate single molecules.

Nanomesh and Nanofibres

(or "Nanofibers") This term covers CNT's (see above), and as described here, the other "nanoscale fibers" referred to as "polymeric" (made from polymers). Currently used in air and liquid filtration applications. Using a process called "electrospinning" - or e-spin - a polymer "mesh" is formed into a nanofiber membrane, hense "nanomesh", with 150 - 200 nm diameters. Some have been made since 1970, but were not called "nano" until recently. One potential use is "to prevent body tissues from sticking together as they heal. It also breaks down in the body over time like biodegradable sutures." which makes it a surgical material for the 21st Century. Other uses include biomedical devices, filtration systems, and dust collecting systems. See Biodegradable nanofiber could prevent scar tissue. "Ultra-Web(R) nanofiber" produced on a Scanning Electron Microscope (SEM).

Nanometer

One billionth of a meter; approximately the length of three to six atoms placed side-by-side, or the width of a single strand of DNA; the thickness of a human hair is between 50,000 and 100,000 nanometers.

2. A unit of spatial measurement that equals one-billionth (10^{-9}) of a meter. The head of a pin is about 1 million nanometers across. A human hair is about 60,000 nanometers in diameter, while a DNA molecule is between 2-12 nanometers wide.

3. One-billionth of a meter, which is approximately the width of 10 hydrogen atoms. The width of the dot above the letter "i" in this sentence is approximately 1 million nanometers. The diameter of an average hair is 50,000 nanometers.

Nanoparticle

A nanoscale spherical or capsule-shaped structure. Most, though not all, nanoparticles are hollow, which provides a central reservoir that can be filled with anticancer drugs, detection agents, or chemicals, known as reporters, that can signal if a drug is having a therapeutic effect. The surface of a nanoparticle can also be adorned with various targeting agents, such as antibodies, drugs, imaging agents, and reporters. Most nanoparticles are constructed to be small enough to pass through blood capillaries and enter cells.

2. In recent years, there has been intense interest in the synthesis and characterization of nanoparticles, which range 1-100 nanometers in diameter. Semiconductor nanoparticles around 1-20 nm in diameter are often called quantum dots, nanocrystals, or Q-particles. These particles possess short-range structures that are essentially the same as the bulk semiconductors, yet have optical or electronic properties that are dramatically different from the bulk properties. The confinement of electrons within a semiconductor nanocrystal results in a shift of the band gap to higher energy with smaller

crystalline size. This effect is known as the quantum size effect. In the strong confinement regime, the actual size of the semiconductor particle determines the allowed energy levels and thus the optical and electronic properties of the material. Due to their finite, small size and the high surface-to-volume ratio, nanoparticles often exhibit novel properties. These properties can ultimately lead to new applications, ranging from catalysis, ceramics, microelectronics, sensors, pigments, and magnetic storage, to drug delivery and biomedical applications. Research in this area is motivated by the possibility of designing nanostructured materials that possess novel electronic, optical, magnetic, mechanical, photochemical, and catalytic properties. Such materials are essential for technological advances in photonics, quantum electronics, nonlinear optics, and information storage and processing.

A wide range of scientifically interesting and technologically important nanoparticles have been produced by both chemical and physical methods.

The synthesis of nanocrystals by colloidal methods involves nucleation (the initial formation of the appropriate semiconductor bond), growth (the formation of a highly crystalline core), and passivation of the nanocrystal surface. The passivation step is important in stabilizing the colloid and controlling the growth of the nanoparticles, preventing the agglomeration and fusing of the particles, and allowing the solubility of the nanoparticles in common solvents. A common approach is to use polymeric surfactants (for example, sodium polyphosphate). The polymer attaches to the surface of the growing particles, usually electrostatically, and prevents their further growth. Another passivation approach is to use capping agents such as thiolates.

In the liquid phase, particle size is controlled by confining the growing particles within micelles or reversed micelles, polymer films, glasses, or zeolites. In the case of micelles, the micellar reagent (for example, dihexadecyl phosphate or dioctadecyldimethylammonium) creates a physical boundary, that is, a well-defined region where the semiconductor is precipitated. In reversed micelles, a small amount of water is mixed with a large amount of an organic solvent and surfactant. The surfactant molecules tend to collect on the surface and stabilize the water drop. The size of the water droplets is directly related to the ratio of the water to the organic phase. Smaller droplets result in smaller nanoparticles. Nanoparticle formation occurs by the reaction of two reagents (one which is soluble only in water and another which is soluble only in the organic solvent). Many nanoparticles have been produced by reverse micelles such as cadmium sulfide, selenide, and telluride, lead sulfide and selenide, and zinc and titanium oxides.

The common chemical synthesis of metallic and intermetallic nanoparticles includes the decomposition of organometallic precursors, such as metal carbonyls (by thermal, photochemical, laser pyrolysis, and ultrasonic methods), to yield the respective elements or alloys, and the reduction of inorganic or organometallic precursors by reducing agents. Different sources of energy can be used to decompose the precursor such as microwave plasma, laser pyrolysis, laser photolysis, and flame combustion. The size of the nanoparticle is determined by the particle residence time, temperature of the chamber, pressure, and precursor composition. Low-temperature flames can also be used to supply the energy to decompose the precursors. Flame synthesis is most common for the production of oxides. Pure metal particles are best produced by gas condensation.

The vapor-phase synthesis of metallic nanoparticles involves evaporation of the material of interest, followed by the condensation of clusters and nanoparticles from the vapor phase. The vapor may be generated with laser or electron beam heating methods. Laser vaporization provides several advantages, including the production of a high-density vapor of any metal, the generation of a directional high-speed metal vapor from a solid target (which can be useful for directional deposition of the particles), control of the evaporation from specific spots on the target, as well as the simultaneous or sequential evaporation of several different targets.

A technique that combines the advantages of pulsed laser vaporization with controlled condensation (LVCC) under well-defined conditions of temperature and pressure has been developed. It allows the synthesis of a wide variety of nanoparticles of metallic, intermetallic, oxides, and carbides of controlled size and composition.

The LVCC method consists of pulsed laser vaporization of a metal or an alloy target into a selected gas mixture in a convective atmosphere created by a temperature gradient between two plates separated by a glass ring (Fig. 1). A pure carrier gas such as helium or argon, or a mixture containing a known composition of a reactant gas (for example, oxygen for the synthesis of oxides, methane for carbides, and so on) can be used. A high-energy pulsed laser (532-nm Nd:YAG laser) with an intensity flux of about 10^6-10^7 W/cm^2 is focused

Fig. 1 Experimental setup for the synthesis of nanoparticles by the laser vaporization controlled-condensation method coupled with a differential mobility analyzer (DMA) for the size selection of the nanoparticles.

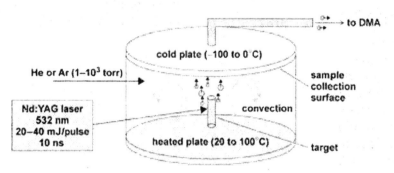

on the target of interest. The resulting plasma causes highly efficient vaporization, and the temperature at the focusing spot can exceed 10,000 K (17,500°F). This high temperature can vaporize all known substances so quickly that the surrounding vapor stays at the ambient temperature. Typical yields are 10^{14}-10^{15} atoms from a surface area of 0.01 cm^2 in a 10^{-8} s pulse. The large temperature gradient between the bottom and top plates results in a steady convection current which moves the nanoparticles away from the nucleation zone (once condensed out of the vapor phase) before they can grow into larger particles. The nanoparticles are deposited as weblike aggregates on the top cold plate (Fig. 2*a*), or transferred in a helium flow to a differential mobility analyzer (DMA) for size selections (Fig. 2*b*). Since the LVCC method produces a significant portion of charged nanoparticles (as ions or free electrons), the DMA classifies and separates the charged nanoparticles based on their electrical mobility in the presence of an electric field.

Fig. 2 Transmission electron micrographs. (*a*) Iron aluminide (FeAl) nanoparticles prepared with the laser vaporization controlled-condensation method with no size selection. The inset showed electron diffraction. (*b*) 20-nm-diameter FeAl nanoparticles selected by the differential mobility analyzer.

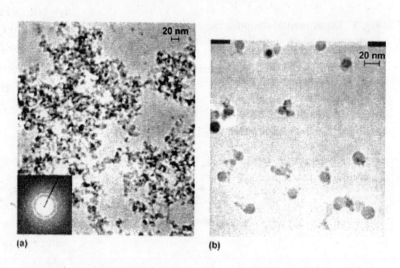

(a)   (b)

The assembly of nanoparticles into filaments and fibers, which retain the unique properties of the nanoparticles, holds promise for the development of novel functional materials and the engineering of a variety of nanodevices and sensors. The nanoparticles can be assembled into long-chain filaments and fibers by applying an electric field during their synthesis by the LVCC method. The filaments can be few centimeters long, and tangle together with neighboring wires to form bundles. Silicon nanoparticles have a tendency to form dendritic structures with unique fractal patterns.

The effect of the electric field on the formation of the chain aggregates acts through the polarization of the charges on the nanoparticles' surface. For larger particles the effect of the electrostatic charge is overpowered by gravity, but for nanoparticles the electrostatic forces are dominant. The nanoparticles' surfaces have a mixture of positive and negative charges, and some of the nanoparticles may have net charges. The dipole force is very strong near the surface of the particle, while farther away from the surface the net charge or monopole force becomes important. These two effects, when combined, may lead to the sticking together of particles of the same net charge.

Semiconductor nanoparticles have technological applications in many areas of optoelectronics such as light-emitting diodes, solid-state lasers, and optical switches. Silicon nanostructures have stimulated much interest due to their unique properties, including single-electron tunneling, nonlinear optical properties, and visible photoluminescence. A transmission electron micrograph and electron diffraction pattern of silicon nanocrystals prepared by the laser vaporization with controlled condensation method. Because of its indirect band gap, bulk silicon does not exhibit visible photoluminescence. The higher energy shift in the photoluminescence of silicon nanocrystals is attributed to the three-dimensional quantum size effect.

Fig. 3 Photoluminescence spectra of silicon nanocrystals suspended in methanol, sulfonated styrene-ethylene/butylenes-styrene triblock copolymer film, and triblock copolymer film containing the silicon nanocrystals.

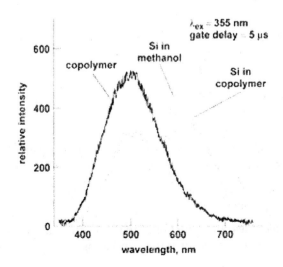

The incorporation of silicon nanocrystals in polymer films may lead to the development of novel materials which combine several properties such as the visible photoluminescence and elasticity. Polymer films containing silicon nanocrystals exhibit the photoluminescence characteristic of the pure polymer and of the suspended silicon nanocrystals (Fig. 3). This may have interesting applications in the design of new materials for optical display and for silicon-based devices in optoelectronics. surface and edge atoms provides active sites for catalyzing surface reactions. Highly nonstoichiometric oxide nanoparticles such as CeO_{2-x} provide a high oxygen-vacancy concentration, and active superoxide surface species. These nanoparticle oxides enable catalytic activation at significantly lower temperatures for the reduction of sulfur dioxide and oxidation of carbon monoxide. Other nanoparticles such as cadmium sulfide and zinc sulfide are efficient photocatalysts for generating hydrogen from water.

Molybdenum and tungsten trioxides are photochromic materials that change color upon oxidation from one state to another by the absorption of light. The photochromic effect is stronger in the nanoparticles than in the bulk material. The photochromic materials have potential practical applications in areas such as displays, imaging devices, "smart windows," and solar energy conversion.

In general, nanostructured materials possess smoother surfaces and enhanced mechanical properties as compared to conventional-grain-size materials. Nanostructured ceramics possess increased ductility since they do not contain many dislocations, and nanoparticles can diffuse fast into the materials' cracks once they are formed. Consolidated intermetallic materials based on nanoparticles show enhanced plasticity; that is, they exhibit significantly better elongations as compared to cast and powder processed components. The filamentlike and treelike assemblies of the nanoparticles may have some special applications as fillers (additives) to increase the elastic modulus (stiffness) and tensile strength (maximum stress before breaking) of low-strength oils and polymeric materials.

Nanoparticles and functionalized nanostructured materials may have a significant impact in biological and biomedical applications. In drug delivery, nanoparticles could be used to deliver drugs where they are needed, avoiding the harmful side effects that often result from potent medicine. Prolonged residence times in blood have been achieved by nanoparticles, allowing the carriers to reach sites throughout the body without premature clearance. Because of the size of the nanoparticles, they can leave the vascular system, especially at sites of disease (such as tumors). Since nanoparticles are much smaller than cells, there is the possibility of subcellular targeting, that is, third-order drug targeting. This is key for gene delivery, where nuclear uptake is a requirement. Since nanoparticles have similar dimensions to natural carriers (for example, lipoproteins and viruses), they may serve as structural models for natural carriers.

Nanomedical technology is opening new avenues in medical diagnostics and disease therapy. Since the size of a quantum dot determines the color it emits after exposure to light, different sizes of dots attached to different biological molecules can be used to track the activities of many tagged molecules simultaneously. Magnetic nanoparticles have been investigated as a potential alternative treatment for cancer. The hyperthermic effect (heat produced by relaxation of the magnetic energy of the magnetic nanoparticles exposed to an alternating magnetic field) can be used to effectively destroy tumor tissue.

Nanopens & Nanopencils

(AKA: Atomic Pencil) "Analogous to using a quill pen but on a billionth the scale", and may transform dip-pen nanolithography. Allows for drawing electronic circuits a thousand times smaller than current ones. The "pen" is an atomic force microscope (AFM).

NanoPGM - nanometer-scale patterned granular motion

The goal of NanoPGM is to generate millions of ìnanofingers,î finger-like structures each only a few nanometers long, that might someday perform precise, massively parallel manipulation of molecules and directed assembly of other nanometer-scale objects. This ability answers one of the biggest technical challenges facing builders of nanocomputers: how to arrange as many as a trillion molecular computing components in an area only a few millimeters square.

Nanopharmaceuticals

nanoscale particles used to modulate drug transport for drug uptake and delivery applications.

Nanopipettes

"Cantilevered/Straight Nanopipettes can be used as nanopens for controlled chemical delivery or removal from regions as small as 100 nanometers. They can also be used as vessels for containing molecules whose optical properties change in response to their chemical environment." Other uses include "controlled chemical etching with the precision of atomic force microscopy; chemical imaging of surfaces; delivering femtosecond laser pulses; and performing NSOM/SNOM imaging using a UV excimer laser." See Cantilevered/Straight Nanopipettes Modifying the nanopipette yields other nanotools, such as Nanotweezers and Nanoheaters. See Nanotools.

Nanoplotter

A multi-tip nanopen. "A device that can draw patterns of tiny lines just 30 molecules thick and a single molecule high. ... produces eight identical patterns at once and extends ... dip-pen nanolithography towards mass producing nanoscale devices and circuits by converting what was a serial process to a parallel one. May be use to "... miniaturize electronic circuits, pattern precise arrays of organic and biomolecules such as DNA and put thousands of different medical sensors on an area much tinier than the head of a pin." See Plotting Chemicals and Nanoplotter with Parallel Writing Capabilities.

Nanopores

Involves squeezing a DNA sequence between two oppositely charged fluid reservoirs, separated by an extremely small channel. Essentially itty bitty tiny holes. Nanoscopic pores found in purpose-built filters, sensors, or diffraction gratings to make them function better. See Influencing structure in the heart of nanoland. As activated carbon, they may also be used as an alternative fuel storage medium, due to their massive internal surface area. "Scientists believe nanopores, tiny holes that allow DNA to pass through one strand at a time, will make DNA sequencing more efficient." See Understanding Nanodevices -- Nanopores. In biology, they are "complex protein assemblies that span cell membranes and allow ionic transport across the otherwise impermeable lipid bilayer. Nanopores are important because while some pores help maintain cell homeostasis, others disrupt cell function." See Towards Fabrication of Solid-State Mimics of Biological Nanopores. "A nanopore can be a protein channel in a lipid bilayer or an extremely small isolated 'hole' in a thin, solid-state membrane" such that "DNA and RNA, can be registered and characterized singly ..." See Developing Nanopores as Probes and The Nanopore Project.

Nanoprobe

Nanoscale machines used to diagnose, image, report on, and treat disease within the body. See "Cell Repair Machine", "Nanites", "Nanobots", and "Nanomachine".

Nanorods or Carbon Nanorods

Formed from multi-wall carbon nanotubes. Another nanoscale material with unique and promising physical properties, such that may yield improvements in high-density data storage, and allow for cheaper flexible solar cells. See Three Element Nanorods and Flexible and Inexpensive Solar Cells Based on Inorganic Nanorods.

Nanoscale

Significantly smaller than a micron; on the scale of large molecules; capable of interacting with molecules; capable of being built by a single assembler.
2. On a scale of nanometers, from atomic dimensions to ~100 nm.

Nanoshell

A nanoparticle composed of a metallic shell surrounding a semiconductor. When nanoshells reach a target cancer cell, they can be irradiated with near-infrared light or excited with a magnetic field, either of which will cause the nanoshell to become hot, killing the cancer cell.

2. Nanoscale metal spheres, which can absorb or scatter light at virtually any wavelength. "The nanoshells act as an amazingly versatile optical component on the nanometer scale: they may provide a whole new approach to optical materials and components," Professor Naomi Halas. See Metal Nanoshells in Bioengineering and Nanoshells May Be Key To Next Wave Of Light-Based Technology and Physics of Nanoshells.

Nanosome
Nanodevices existing symbiotically inside biological cells, doing mechanosynthesis and disassembly for it and replicating with the cell. Similar to nanochondria.

Nanosources
Sources that emit light from nanometre-scale volumes.

Nanosprings
A nanowire wrapped into a helix. Speculation is that they "may someday make highly sensitive magnetic field detectors, perhaps finding application in hard drive read heads. Alternatively, nanosprings could serve as positioners, or even as tiny conventional springs, for nanomachines of the future." See Spiraling in on Nanosprings and Nanosprings jump into place.

Nanosurgery
A generic term including molecular repair and cell surgery.

Nanosystem
A eutactic set of nanoscale components working together to serve a set of purposes; complex nanosystems can be of macroscopic size.

Nanotechism
The religion of nanotech, as opposed to the science of nanotech.

Nanotechnology
In recent general usage, any technology related to features of

nanometer scale: thin films, fine particles, chemical synthesis, advanced microlithography, and so forth. As introduced by the author, a technology based on the ability to build structures to complex, atomic specifications by means of mechanosynthesis; this can be termed molecular nanotechnology.

2. The interactions of cellular and molecular components and engineered materials—typically clusters of atoms, molecules, and molecular fragments—at the most elemental level of biology. Such nanoscale objects—typically, though not exclusively, with dimensions smaller than 100 nanometers—can be useful by themselves or as part of larger devices containing multiple nanoscale objects.

3. The science of manipulating atoms and molecules to fabricate materials, devices and systems. Unlike current production methods, in which existing parts and components are combined, nanotechnology takes atoms and precisely assembles them to produce items with desirable characteristics. Objects are built in a manner similar to the way bricks are stacked on top of one another to build a wall. According to the Oxford English Dictionary, the term "nanotechnology" was coined in 1974.

4. A manufacturing technology able to inexpensively fabricate most structures consistent with natural law, and to do so with molecular precision.

5. Systems for transforming matter, energy, and information, based on nanometer-scale components with precisely defined molecular features. The term nanotechnology has also been used more broadly to refer to techniques that produce or measure features less than 100 nanometers in size; this meaning embraces advanced microfabrication and metrology. Although complex systems with precise molecular features cannot be made with existing techniques, they can be designed and analyzed. Studies of nanotechnology in this sense remain theoretical, but are intended to guide the development of practical technological systems.

Comparisons with existing systems

The nature of nanotechnological systems can best be understood through comparisons with more familiar systems such as biological cells and industrial factories. Biological cells are most nearly analogous in their scale and use of molecular components. Cells contain millions to billions of precisely structured molecular devices, such as enzymes and ribosomes. Bacterial cells typically contain about a million bytes of digital information [stored in deoxyribonucleic acid (DNA)], and many are able to swim by turning a helical protein propeller (a flagellum) using a reversible, variable-speed motor (the flagellar motor). The molecular "machine" systems of a biological cell are able, taken as a whole, to construct all the parts needed to make a new cell. Biology thus demonstrates that molecular machine systems are possible, that they can read and write information in molecular form, and that they can, in some instances, produce additional molecular machine systems at low cost.

Artificial molecular machine systems share these characteristics of biological systems. They differ, however, both in components and in overall organization. Rather than transporting molecules by diffusion through a liquid, they could transport them by using mechanical conveyors in small evacuated volumes; rather than using folded polymers (such as proteins) as structural materials, they could use strong, ceramiclike materials. In overall organization, they resemble machines and factories rather than cells and organisms.

Conceived molecular manufacturing systems use gears, shafts, bearings, belts, electric motors, computers, robotic positioning mechanisms, and the like to transform matter, energy, and information. Their components resemble those of conventional machine systems. For example, a design for a gearbox for transforming shaft power from higher to lower angular speeds would consist of a rigid framework supporting input and output shafts mounted on bearings. The gears have teeth and obey the usual rules regarding gear ratios. In detail, however, the differences are substantial: each gear tooth typically consists of a single row of atoms, and the smoothness of interatomic force fields enables gears and bearings to operate without an added lubricant. The design for typical moving parts specifies measurements in nanometers, with the parts containing several thousand atoms. Systems containing enough parts to serve the function of an assembly robot or a computer require several million to several billion atoms, and their volumes occupy a significant fraction of a cubic micrometer. Molecular machine systems differ greatly from existing micromachines: the latter are typically made with lithographic technologies, are many micrometers in scale, contain a billion times as much matter as a comparable molecular machine, and are imprecise on a molecular scale.

Basic principles

Nanotechnology based on molecular manufacturing requires a combination of familiar chemical and mechanical principles in unfamiliar applications. In conventional chemistry, molecules move by diffusion and encounter each other in all possible positions and orientations. The resulting chemical reactions are accordingly hard to direct. Molecular manufacturing, in contrast, can exploit mechanosynthesis, that is, using mechanical devices to guide the motions of reactive molecules. By applying the conventional mechanical principle of grasping and positioning to conventional chemical reactions, mechanosynthesis can provide an unconventional ability to cause molecular changes to occur at precise locations in a precise sequence. Reliable positioning is required in order for mechanosynthetic processes to construct objects with millions to billions of precisely arranged atoms.

Mechanosynthetic systems are intended to perform several basic functions. Their first task is to acquire raw materials from an externally provided source, typically a liquid solution containing a variety of useful molecular species. The second task is to process these raw materials through steps that separate molecules of different kinds, bind them reliably to specific sites, and then (often) transform them into highly active chemical species, such as radicals, carbenes, and strained alkenes and alkynes. Finally, mechanical devices can apply these bound, active species to a workpiece in a controlled position and orientation and deposit or remove a precise number of atoms of specific kinds at specific locations.

To support these functions, it is necessary to provide appropriate mechanisms and conditions. Binding, transforming, and moving molecules can best be accomplished by nanoscale molecular machinery. To minimize friction, contamination, and side reactions, the ideal environment is vacuum, which requires a suitable enclosure and pumping mechanisms. If a mechanosynthetic system must build complex products (rather than performing simple, repetitive operations), a device resembling an industrial assembly robot can be used, requiring a source of instructions to guide its sequence of movements.

Successful designs must overcome several challenges to reliable operation. These fall into several classes.

Both quantum-mechanical uncertainty and thermal vibration cause random displacements in the positions of parts. For nanomechanical parts at room temperature, thermal vibration is overwhelmingly more important than quantum uncertainty. Because the mean-square displacement of a part is inversely proportional to the stiffness of the structure that holds it in place, the amplitude of thermal vibration can be limited by careful design. In mechanosynthetic systems, typical vibrational amplitudes can be limited to less than one-tenth of an atomic radius. Because the probability of displacement has a gaussian distribution, transient misalignments as large as an atomic diameter can be made extremely rare.

Infrequent, high-amplitude thermal vibrations can break even strong chemical bonds. Breaking a single bond in a molecular machine will typically cause it to fail. In the terrestrial ambient background radiation environment, however, structures with reasonable thermal stability will experience bond breakage chiefly from ionizing radiation. The rate of device damage due to ionizing radiation is roughly proportional to device mass, and devices on a scale of hundreds of nanometers will last many decades in the terrestrial environment. To be reliable, larger systems either must be made of parts large enough to tolerate some damage or must be organized redundantly so that the system itself can tolerate some failed parts. Photochemical damage can be prevented by enclosing systems in opaque shields; aluminum 0.25 micrometer thick is ample for long-term protection in full sunlight.

Reliable molecular manufacturing systems have strong similarities to digital computers. In conventional materials processing, as in analog electronics, all operations are imprecise. Each object produced has a unique size, shape, composition, and microstructure, differing both from the ideal design and from all previous objects. In molecular manufacturing, though, as in digital electronics, each operation is either entirely correct or clearly wrong. The result of a digital logic operation is a specific pattern of ones and zeros. No stable intermediate states are possible, and physical principles enable the design of circuits that produce the correct pattern with high reliability. Similarly, the result of a molecular manufacturing operation is a specific pattern of bonded atoms. For suitable choices of product structure, no stable intermediate states are possible, and once again, physical principles enable the design of processes that produce the correct pattern with high reliability.

Applications

Much as digital computers provide a general capability for manipulating information, molecular manufacturing can provide a general capability for manipulating matter. For both digital computers and molecular manufacturing (unlike an adding machine or a lathe), it is difficult to describe the range of applications. This section touches on only a few of the most prominent.

Because molecular manufacturing can make precise, nanoscale features, it can be used to fabricate improved circuitry for digital logic. It is widely recognized that diamond would be superior to silicon for this purpose, if it could be fabricated with comparable ease. Molecular manufacturing can make this practical. Design calculations based on simpler, mechanical nanocomputers place a lower bound on what can be achieved. It appears feasible to build a central processing unit for a computer that occupies a volume less than 1 cubic micrometer, consumes roughly 100 microwatts of power, and executes about 1 billion instructions per second.

Nanotechnologies based on molecular manufacturing are focused on superior molecular-scale sensing and manipulation in order to allow development of a broad range of novel scientific and medical instruments. In particular, the goal is to enable scientists to probe the molecular structure of cells, providing data regarding structure and function at the molecular level in a more direct manner. The application of this knowledge to medicine is being directed at the development of nanoscale medical devices of greater complexity and capability than modern drug molecules, and

of far greater precision than modern surgical instruments. Implementation strategies
Several technology trends are converging on nanotechnologies; the most important being miniaturization of semiconductor structures, driven by progress in microelectronics. More directly relevant are efforts to extend chemical synthesis to the construction of larger and more complex molecular objects. Protein engineering and supramolecular chemistry are active fields that exploit weak intermolecular forces to organize small parts into larger structures. Scanning probe microscopes are used to move individual atoms and molecules.

Nanoterrorism
Using MNT derived nanites to do damage to people or places.

Nano-test-tubes
Opening and Filling of Multi-Walled Carbon Nanotubes (MWTs) and The Opening and Filling of Single-Walled Carbon Nanotubes (SWTs). A High Resolution Transition Electron Micrograph (TEM) of Samarium Oxide Inside a Multi-Walled Carbon Nanotube.

Nanotube
A tiny, hollow cylinder with an outside diameter of a nanometer that is formed spontaneously from atoms such as carbon. When aligned in a certain way, their atoms can conduct electricity as effectively as copper. Aligned in a slightly different way, they are electrical semiconductors-midway between conductors and insulators. Nanotubes are also stronger than steel, so long filaments can be used to create super-tough lightweight materials.
2. A one dimensional fullerene (a convex cage of atoms with only hexagonal and/or pentagonal faces) with a cylindrical shape. Carbon nanotubes discovered in 1991 by Sumio Iijima resemble rolled up graphite, although they can not really be made that way. Depending on the direction that the tubes appear to have been rolled (quantified by the 'chiral vector'), they are known to act as conductors or semiconductors. Nanotubes are a proving to be useful as molecular components for nanotechnology.

Nanowire

A nanometer-scale wire made of metal atoms, silicon, or other materials that conduct electricity. Nanowires are built atom by atom on a solid surface, often as part of a microfluidic device. They can be coated with molecules such as antibodies that will bind to proteins and other substances of interest to researchers and clinicians. By the very nature of their nanoscale size, nanowires are incredibly sensitive to such binding events and respond by altering the electrical current flowing through them, and thus can form the basis of ultra sensitive molecular detectors.

2. "Semiconductor nanowires are one-dimensional structures, with unique electrical and optical properties, that are used as building blocks in nanoscale devices." See Nanowires within nanowires and Learning how to Fabricate Nanowire. "Striped or 'superlatticed' nanowires can function as transistors, LEDs (light-emitting diodes) and other optoelectronic devices, biochemical sensors, heat-pumping thermoelectric devices, or all of the above, along the same length of wire."

Nanowetting

How wetting behavior depends on nanoscale topography on a substrate.

NBIC

Nanotechnology, Biotechnology, Information Technology and Cognitive Science.

NEMS - nanoelectromechanical systems

A generic term to describe nano scale electrical/mechanical devices.

NE3LS

Nanotechnology's Ethical, Environmental, Economic, Legal, and Social Implications. From 'Mind the gap': science and ethics in nanotechnology.

NMOS

An acronym for n-channel metal-oxide-semiconductor, as in NMOS transistor and NMOS logic.

Nucleus

The positively charged core of an atom, an object of ~0.00001 atomic diameters containing >99.9% of the atomic mass. Nuclear positions define atomic positions.

OLED or Organic

LED is not made of semiconductors. It's made from carbon-based molecules. That is the key science factor that leads to potentially eliminating LEDs' biggest drawback ñ size. The carbon-based molecules are much smaller. And according to a paper written by Dr. Uwe Hoffmann, Dr. Jutta Trube and Andreas Kl-ppel, entitled OLED - A bright new idea for flat panel displays "OLED is brighter, thinner, lighter, and faster than the normal liquid crystal (LCD) display in use today. They also need less power to run, offer higher contrast, look just as bright from all viewing angles and are - potentially - a lot cheaper to produce than LCD screens."

Olefin

An alkene.

OMEGA POINT

Also called the Quantum Omega Point Theory. A possible future state when intelligence controls the Universe totally, and the amount of information processed and stored goes asymptotically towards infinity.

Omitted reaction

A chemical reaction that fails by not occurring (see misreaction).

Orbital Tower

Also known as a "space tether", "beanstalk" or "heavenly

funicular". A cable in synchronous orbit, with one end anchored to the surface of the Earth, often with a small asteroid at the outer end to provide some extra tension and stability. Picture also a "space elevator". In theory, constructed of a diamondoid material, approximately 22,000 miles long, with one end in a stable orbit, and the other somewhere [probably] around the equator. Used frequently in science-fiction yarns, and may become a reality with the advent of mature MNT. Such an elevator would move freight and passengers into orbit at a cost per pound orders of magnitude less than current launches, with passenger safety comparable to train, plane, or subway trips. Becomes possible when we can mass-produce nanotubes, and make their length to fit.

Orbital

In the approximation that each electron in a molecule has a distinct, independent wave function, the spatial distribution of an electron wave function corresponds to a molecular orbital. These, in turn, can be approximated as sums of contributions from the orbitals characteristic of the isolated atoms. An electron added to a molecule--or, similarly, one excited to a higher-energy state within a molecule--would occupy a state with a different wave function from the rest; an unoccupied state of this kind corresponds to an unoccupied molecular orbital. Orbital-symmetry effects on reaction rates arise when a reaction requires overlap between two lobes of the orbitals on each of two reagents: if the algebraic signs of the wave functions in the facing lobes do not match, bond formation between those orbitals is prohibited.

Overlap

Orbitals lack sharply defined surfaces, declining in amplitude exponentially in their surface regions. When two orbitals are brought together, regions of substantial amplitude overlap. The resulting system can be described as two new orbitals, one formed by joining the two original orbitals without introducing a node in the wave function, and the other formed with a node between them. The nodeless joining reduces the energy of the electrons relative to the separate orbitals, resulting in a bonding interaction; joining with a node raises the energy, producing an antibonding interaction. If both new orbitals are occupied, antibonding forces dominate, resulting in overlap repulsion. Molecular mechanics models give an approximate description of overlap (and other) forces for a certain range of atoms and geometries.

Overlap repulsion

A repulsive force resulting from the nonbonding overlap of two atoms.

P

Paradigm Shift

When one conceptual world-view is replaced by another, or, a change of patterns on a massive scale. When Copernicus showed how the Earth rotates around the Sun, and not vice versa, that created a paradigm shift [it forced a new way of thinking about our place in the Universe]. And when quantum physics and general relativity displaced Newtonian mechanics, that created another shift. Applied to an enabling technology such as molecular manufacturing, it suggests that there will be many shifts occurring, soon, and with wide-ranging and often disruptive consequences.

Partition function

A function determined by the probability distribution (over phase space in the classical treatment; over quantum states in the quantum treatment) describing a thermally equilibrated system; many thermodynamic quantities can be expressed in terms of the partition function and its derivatives.

PDF

See probability density function.

Pervasive Computing

When computers (and sensors and actuators) become virtually invisible, and are used in almost every aspect of human commerce, interaction, and life. It will allow you full control over data and information, enabling you to send, receive, manage, and update your data from anywhere at any time. It will also allow you full control over your environment, in so far as you will be able to speak or gesture commands, effecting changes to things around you. Applications include: environmental monitoring - when you enter a room, they sense your presence and adjust temperature and humidity to your personal preferences; building security - to sense chemical weapons and perform face recognition; information transfer - allowing you to send and receive calls, data, and images from anywhere to anywhere, without the need of bulky equipment. Also called "Ubiquitous Computing", "Intelligent Telesensing", "Proactive Computing", "Distributed Information Management Systems", "The Evernet", and "Calm Technology". "...it will look like nothing to the naked eye. ...beneath the surface, tiny computing networks will be doing exactly what we want them to do - working behind the scenes to help us see clearer, travel safer, and place more knowledge, rather than frustration, into our heads."

Peptide
A short chain of amino acids; see protein.

PES
See potential energy surface.

Phase space
A classical system of N particles can be described by its 3N position and 3N momentum coordinates. The phase space associated with the system is the 6N dimensional space defined by these coordinates.

Phonon
A quantum of acoustic energy, analogous to the quantum of electromagnetic radiation, the photon. Thermal excitations in a crystal or in an elastic continuum can be described as a population of phonons (analogous to blackbody electromagnetic radiation). In highly inhomogeneous solids, a description in terms of phonons breaks down and localized vibrational modes become important.

Pico Technology

(trillionth of a meter) -- the next step smaller, after Nano-technology. The art of manipulating materials on a quantum scale.

Pink Goo

(humorous) Humans (in analogy with grey goo). "Pink Goo to refer to Old Testament apes who see their purpose as being fruitful and multiplying, filling up of the cosmos with lots more such apes, unmodified."

Pi bond

A covalent bond formed by overlap between two p orbitals on different atoms (see sp). Pi bonds are superimposed on sigma bonds, forming double or triple bonds.

Poisson's ratio

A bar of an isotropic, elastic material ordinarily shrinks laterally when it is stretched longitudinally. The lateral contracting strain divided by the applied tensile strain is Poisson's ratio, which varies from material to material.

Polycyclic

A cyclic structure contains rings of bonds; a structure having many such rings is termed polycyclic. In the polycyclic structures of interest in this volume, a large fraction of the atoms are members of multiple small rings, resulting in considerable rigidity.

Polysilicon

Short for Polycrystalline Silicon, used in the manufacture of computer chips.

Positional Controlled Chemical Synthesis or Positional Synthesis

Control of chemical reactions by precisely positioning the reactive molecules, the basic principle of assemblers.

Positional Assembly

Constructing materials an atom or molecule at a time.

Positional synthesis

Control of chemical reactions by precisely positioning the reactive molecules; the basic principle of assemblers.

POSS Nanotechnology

Short for Polyhedral Oligomeric Silsesquioxanes Nanotechnology. POSS nanomaterials are attractive for missile and satellite launch rocket applications because they offer effective protection from collisions with space debris and the extreme thermal environments of deep space and atmospheric re-entry. Another application of POSS nanotechnology under development is a new high-temperature lubricant. This new nanolubricant is effective at temperatures up to 500fF, which is 100fF greater than conventional lubricants.

Posthuman

Persons of unprecedented physical, intellectual, and psychological capacity, self-programming, self-constituting, potentially immortal, unlimited individuals.

Post Monetary Economy

After the advent of mature Nanotechnology, it is likely that our economic reality will change, possibly to the extent of eliminating currency as we know it today.

Potential energy

The energy associated with a configuration of particles, as distinct from their motions. In macroscopic experience, potential energy can be increased (for example) by stretching a spring or by lifting a mass against a gravitational force; in molecular systems, potential energy can be increased (for example) by stretching a bond or by separating molecules against a van der Waals attraction.

Potential energy surface

The potential energy of a ground-state molecular system containing N atoms is a function of its geometry, defined by 3N spatial coordinates (a configuration space). If the energy is imagined as corresponding to a height in a 3N + 1 dimensional space, the resulting landscape of hills, hollows, and valleys is the potential energy surface.

Potential well

In a potential energy surface, the region surrounding a local energy minimum. Typically taken to include at least those points in configuration space such that a path of steadily declining energy can be found that leads to the minimum in question, and such that no similar path can be found to any other minimum. If the PES were a landscape, this would be the region around the minimum that could be filled with water without any flowing down and away toward another minimum.

Probability density function

Consider an uncertain physical property and a corresponding space describing the range of values that the property can have (e.g., the configuration of a thermally excited N particle system and the corresponding 3N dimensional configuration space). The probability density function associated with a property is defined over the corresponding space; its value at a particular point is the probability per unit volume that the property has a value in an infinitesimal region around that point.

Protein

Living cells contain many molecules that consist of amino acid polymers folded to form more-or-less definite three-dimensional structures; these are termed proteins. Short polymers lacking definite three-dimensional structures are termed peptides. Many proteins incorporate structures other than amino acids, either as covalently attached side chains or as bound ligands. Molecular objects made of protein form much of the molecular machinery of living cells.

Protein design, protein engineering

The design and construction of new proteins; an enabling technology for nanotechnology.

Protein Folding

"The process by which proteins acquire their functional, preordained, three-dimensional structure after they emerge, as linear polymers of amino acids, from the ribosome."

Proteomics

The term proteome refers to all the proteins expressed by a genome, and thus proteomics involves the identification of proteins in the body and the determination of their role in physiological and pathophysiological functions. ... Ultimately it is believed that through proteomics new disease markers and drug targets can be identified that will help design products to prevent, diagnose and treat disease.

Proximal probes

A family of devices capable of fine positional control and sensing, including scanning tunneling and atomic force microscopes; an enabling technology for nanotechnology.

Quantum

Describes a system of particles in terms of a wave function defined over the configuration of particles having distinct locations is implicit in the potential energy function that determines the wave function, the observable dynamics of the motion of such particles from point to point. In describing the energies, distributions and behaviours of electrons in nanometer-scale structures, quantum mechanical methods are necessary. Electron wave functions help determine the potential energy surface of a molecular system, which in turn is the basis for classical descriptions of molecular motion. Nanomechanical systems can almost always be described in terms of classical mechanics, with occasional quantum mechanical corrections applied within the framework of a classical model.

QuantumBrain

[theoretical] Think of your brain. Now, think of your brain performing at vastly superior levels. Nanobots will become an as-needed addition to your existing neurons, extending your mental capacities further then you can probably now imagine. .

Quantum Computer

A computer that takes advantage of quantum mechanical properties such as superposition and entanglement resulting from nanoscale, molecular, atomic and subatomic components. Quantum computers may revolutionize the computer industry in the not too distant future.

Quantum Confined Atoms (QCA)

Atoms caged inside nanocrystals. May find uses in clear-glass sunglasses, bio-sensors, and optical computing.

Quantum Cryptography

A system based on quantum- mechanical principles. Eavesdroppers alter the quantum state of the system and so are detected. Developed by Brassard and Bennett, only small laboratory demonstrations have been made.

Quantum mechanics

Quantum mechanics describes a system of particles in terms of a wave function defined over the configuration space of the system. Although the concept of particles having distinct locations is implicit in the potential energy function that determines the wave function (e.g., of a ground-state system), the observable dynamics of the system cannot be described in terms of the motion of such particles from point to point. In describing the energies, distributions, and behaviors of electrons in nanometer-scale structures, quantum mechanical methods are necessary. Electron wave functions help determine the potential energy surface of a molecular system, which in turn is the basis for classical descriptions of molecular motion. Nanomechanical systems can almost always be described in terms of classical mechanics, with occasional quantum mechanical corrections applied within the framework of a classical model.

2. A largely computational physical theory explaining the behavior of quantum phenomena, which incorporates the theory of special relativity. Despite dilignet attempts, general relativity has not been sucessfully incorporated into quantum mechanics.

Quantum dot (Qdots)

Nanometer sized semiconductor particles, made of cadmium selenide (CdSe), cadmium sulfide (CdS) or cadmium telluride

(CdTe) with an inert polymer coating. The semiconductor material used for the core is chosen based upon the emission wavelength range being targeted: CdS for UV-blue, CdSe for the bulk of the visible spectrum, CdTe for the far red and near-infrared, with the particle's size determining the exact color of a given quantum dot. The polymer coating safeguards cells from cadmium toxicity but also affords the opportunity to attach any variety targeting molecules, including monoclonal antibodies directed to tumor-specific biomarkers. Because of their small size, quantum dots can function as cell- and even molecule-specific markers that will not interfere with the normal workings of a cell. In addition, the availability of quantum dots of different colors provides a powerful tool for following the actions of multiple cells and molecules simultaneously.

2. Nanometer-sized semiconductor crystals, or electrostatically confined electrons. Something (usually a semiconductor island) capable of confining a single electron, or a few, and in which the electrons occupy discrete energy states just as they would in an atom (quantum dots have been called "artificial atoms"). [CMP] Other terminology reflects the preoccupations of different branches of research: microelectronics folks may refer to a "single-electron transistor" or "controlled potential barrier," whereas quantum physicists may speak of a "Coulomb island" or "zero-dimensional gas" and chemists may speak of a "colloidal nanoparticle" or "semiconductor nanocrystal." All of these terms are, at various times, used interchangeably with "quantum dot," and they refer more or less to the same thing: a trap that confines electrons in all three dimensions.

Quantum Dot Nanocrystals (QDNs)

Used to tag biological molecules, and "measuring between five and ten nanometres across, are made up of three components. Their cores contain paired clusters of atoms such as cadmium and selenium that combine to create a semiconductor. This releases light of a specific colour when stimulated by ultraviolet of a wide range of frequencies. These clusters are surrounded by a shell made of an inorganic substance, to protect them. The whole thing is then coated with an organic surface, to allow the attachment of proteins or DNA molecules. By varying the number of atoms in the core, QDNs can be made to emit light of different colours."

Quantum Mirage
A nanoscale property that may allow information to be transfered through use of the wave property of electrons. Thus, quantum computers might not require wires as we know them.

Quantum Tunneling
When electrons pass through a barrier, without overcoming it or breaking it down.

Quantum Well
A P-N-P junction in which the "N" layer is ~10 nm (where traditional physics leaves off and quantum effects take over) and an "electron trap" is created. "If one makes a heterostructure with sufficiently thin layers, quantum interference effects begin to appear prominently in the motion of the electrons. The simplest structure in which these may be observed is a quantum well, which simply consists of a thin layer of a narrower-gap semiconductor between thicker layers of a wider-gap material."

Quantum Wire
Another form of quantum dot, but unlike the single-dimension "dot," a quantum wire is confined only in two dimensions - that is it has "length," and allows the electrons to propagate in a "particle-like" fashion. Constructed typically on a semiconductor base, and (among other things) used to produce very intense laser beams, switchable up to multi-gigahertz per second.

Qubit
The quantum computing analog to a bit. Qubits exhibit superposition. Thus, unlike normal bits, qubits can be both 1 and 0 at the same time.

Radiation damage

Chemical changes (bond breakage, ionization) caused by high-energy radiation (e.g., x-rays, gamma rays, high-speed electrons, protons, etc.).

Radical

A structure with an unpaired electron (but excluding certain metal ions). In organic molecules, a radical is often associated with a highly reactive site of reduced valence (see doublet). The term radical is sometimes used to describe a substructure within a molecule; the term free radical then describes a radical in this sense, viewed as the result of cleaving the bond linking the substructure to the rest of the molecule.

Reaction

A process that transforms one or more chemical species into others. Typical reactions make or break bonds; others change the state of ionization or other properties taken to distinguish chemical species.

Reagent

A chemical species that undergoes change as a result of a chemical reaction.

Reagent device

A large reagent structure (or a large structure that binds a smaller reagent) serving as a component of a mechanochemical system. A reagent device exists chiefly to hold, position, and manipulate the environment of a reagent moiety.

Reagent moiety
The portion of a reagent device that is intimately involved in a chemical reaction.

Receptor
A structure that can capture a molecule (often of a specific type in a specific orientation) owing to complementary surface shapes, charge distributions, and so forth, without forming a covalent bond. See dissociation constant.

Reconstruction
A crystal consists of a regular array of atoms, and the simplest model of a crystal surface would be generated by simply discarding all atoms to one side of a surface without changing the positions of the rest. In reality, however, the positions of the remaining atoms do change. A pattern of displacements that lowers the symmetry of the surface (relative to the ideally terminated crystal) is termed a surface reconstruction; some reconstructions alter the pattern of bonds.

Red Goo
Deliberately designed and released destructive nanotechnology, as opposed to accidentally created grey goo.

Reduced mass
Many dynamical properties of a system consisting of two interacting masses, $m1$ and $m2$, are equivalent to those of a system in which one mass is fixed in space and the other has a mass (the reduced mass) with the value $m1m2/(m1 + m2)$. The reduced mass description has fewer dynamical variables.

Register
A temporary storage location for an array of bits within a digital logic system.

Relaxation time
A measure of the rate at which a disequilibrium distribution decays toward an equilibrium distribution. The electron

relaxation time in a metal, for example, describes the time required for a disequilibrium distribution of electron momenta (e.g., in a flowing current) to decay toward equilibrium in the absence of an ongoing driving force and can be interpreted as the mean time between scattering events for a given electron.

Replicator

A system able to build copies of itself when provided with raw materials and energy.

Representative point

The point in a configuration space that represents the geometry of a system.

Ribosome

A naturally occurring molecular machine that manufactures proteins according to instructions derived from the cell's genes.

Rigid structure

As used in this volume, a covalent structure that is reasonably stiff. In a typical rigid structure, all modes of deformation encounter first-order restoring forces resulting from some combination of bond stretching and angle bending; such a structure cannot undergo deformation by bond torsion alone. Meeting this condition usually requires a polycyclic diamondoid structure.

S

Salt bridge
An ionic bond between charged groups that are part of larger covalent structures; salt bridges occur in many proteins.

SAMFET
(self assembled monolayer field effect transistor). Where a few molecules act as FETs, exhibiting both very strong gain, and extraordinarily rapid response.

Saturated
An organic molecule is described as saturated if it is a closed shell species lacking double or triple bonds; forming a new bond to a saturated molecule requires the cleavage of an existing bond.

Scanning Capacitance Microscopy
A method for mapping the local capacitance of a surface.

Scanning Force Microscope (SFM)
An instrument able to image surfaces to molecular accuracy by mechanically probing their surface contours. A kind of proximal probe. .... A device in which the deflection of a sharp stylus mounted on a soft spring is monitored as the stylus is moved across a surface. If the deflection is kept constant by moving the surface up and down by measured increments, the result (under favorable conditions) is an atomic-resolution topographic map of the surface. Also termed an atomic force microscope.

Scanning Near Field Optical Microscopy

A method for observing local optical properties of a surface that can be smaller than the wavelength of the light used.

Scanning Thermal Microscopy

A method for observing local temperatures and temperature gradients on a surface.

Scanning tunneling microscope

A device in which a sharp conductive tip is moved across a conductive surface close enough to permit a substantial tunneling current (typically a nanometer or less). In a common mode of operation, the voltage is kept constant and the current is monitored and kept constant by controlling the height of the tip above the surface; the result, under favorable conditions, is an atomic-resolution map of the surface reflecting a combination of topography and electronic properties. The STM has been used to manipulate atoms and molecules on surfaces.

2. An instrument able to image conducting surfaces to atomic accuracy; has been used to pin molecules to a surface.

The STM works by applying a very small voltage to the tip and causing a small quantum mechanical tunneling current to jump the gap between the tip and the sample. This current is then used to create a topographical map of the surface (a feedback circuit controls the tip to minimize current variations, and this information is used for the map). Increasing the voltage enables a researcher to move atoms around, pile them up, or trigger chemical reactions.

3. An instrument able to image conducting surfaces to atomic accuracy; has been used to pin molecules to a surface.

4. A device for imaging the surface of conductors and semiconductors with atomic resolution. Due to its relatively simple construction and operation and its ability to achieve atomic resolution with relative ease, the scanning tunneling microscope (STM) has gained worldwide acceptance by scientists studying surface phenomena.

Principles of operation

The operating principles of the scanning tunneling microscope are illustrated in Fig. 1. A wire made of tungsten, gold, or some other noble metal is etched electrochemically at one end down to a fine tip whose radius is 0.1 micrometer, or less; it is then attached onto a piezoelectrically scanned (*x,y,z*) stage. Under a powerful microscope, such as a transmission electron microscope, the tip of the wire typically looks as illustrated in Fig. 1, with one atom always protruding farther from the surface. The piezoelectric tripod can be scanned in *x*, *y*, or *z* over distances of up to 100 µ with a resolution far better than 0.1 nanometer (approximately one-half the diameter of typical atoms) by applying a voltage across its *x*, *y*, or *z* electrode, respectively. A voltage *V* in the range of 10 mV is applied between the wire tip and the conducting sample to be imaged, and the piezoelectric *z*-scanner is used to move the tip gently toward the sample. As the end atom on the tip approaches to within a few atomic diameters of a sample atom, electrons can tunnel from the tip to the sample (or vice versa) through the potential barrier imposed by the work functions of the tip and sample, thereby generating a current, which is typically of the order of nanoamperes.

Fig. 1 Schematic diagram of the scanning tunneling microscope showing the configuration of the piezoelectric tripod, wire tip, and sample.

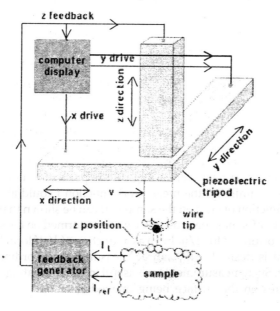

The tunnel current I_t increases exponentially with decreasing spacing z between tip and sample atom. For small applied bias υ voltages , the tunnel current is given by the equation below,

$$I_t = f(\nu)\exp -(A\phi^{1/2}z)$$

where u is the mean of the work functions of the tip and sample, A is a constant equal to $(4\,ph)(2m)^{1/2}$, m is the electronic mass, h is is Planck's constant, and $F(\upsilon)$ is the overlap integral of the local density of states of tip and sample taken over the energies between the Fermi levels of the tip and the sample. For a typical tip-sample combination, the tunnel current I_t decreases by a factor of 10 for every 0.1 nm increase in spacing z. For this reason, a negligible contribution to the tunnel current I_t is provided by electron tunneling from other atoms on the tip since the other atoms lie farther from the sample than the atom that protrudes from the tip.

In the scanning tunnel microscope, the tunnel current I_t is compared with a constant reference current (I_{ref}); the error signal so generated is used to move the z-piezoelectric scanner up or down (thereby increasing or decreasing z) in order to maintain a constant tunnel current as the tip is raster-scanned in x and y to record an image. The tunneling image is usually recorded on a computer as variations in the z position (measured through the z-piezoelectric voltage) corresponding to each (x,y) coordinate of the tip. For metallic surfaces such as gold, the local density of states is a weak function of the applied bias voltage, and the overlap integral $f(u)$ has no structure; it varies linearly with voltage, yielding a voltage-independent tunneling conductance. In these cases the variations in z closely approximate the atomic topography of the surface. However, for more complex surfaces, $f(\upsilon)$ is no and furthermore can vary from one (x,y) location on the sample to the next, depending on the particular atom being probed. Similarly, the mean work function f could also vary as a function of (x,y) on the sample. It can be shown that local-density-of-states spectroscopy can be performed on the sample by recording $(d \ln I_t)/(d \ln V)$ as a function of V. If local barrier height is desired, $Af^{1/2}$ can be measured by recording $(d \ln I_t)/dz$. Such measurements are useful in differentiating atomic features on the surface being imaged.

Other areas of application of the scanning tunneling microscope are in the study of electrochemical processes and biological imaging. It is also being used for surface modifications on an atomic scale.

The success of the scanning tunneling microscope has led to the development of many novel scanned probe microscopes that use the same piezoelectric scanning and feedback principles but rely on different mechanisms of tip-sample interaction to generate the error signal that controls the tip-sample spacing and hence the image. One scanning probe microscope that has been particularly successful is the atomic force microscope. In this microscope (Fig. 2) the interaction mechanism sensed is the repulsive force between the charge clouds of the tip atom and the sample atoms. Because this interaction does not rely on a tunneling current, the atomic force microscope can image both conducting and insulating surfaces with atomic resolution. In the early versions of the atomic force microscope, a diamond tip was attached onto a gold foil, and the repulsive force between tip and sample was

Fig. 2 Schematic diagram of the atomic force microscope.

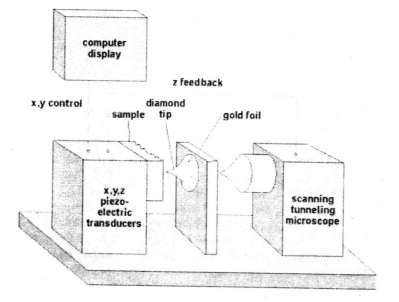

detected through the deflection of the gold foil, which in turn
was sensed by using a scanning tunneling microscope. If the
gold foil has a spring constant of 10 newtons/m, a force of
10^{-9} N will result in a deflection of 0.1 nm, which is easily
detectable with a tunneling microscope. Later experiments
have used silicon micromechanical cantilevers with integrated
silicon tips and laser probes for sensing the deflection. Typically
tracking forces are in the range of 10^{-7} N for instruments
operating in air and 10^{-9} N under water. Applications include
the imaging of the atomic arrangement of insulating crystal
surfaces and the high-resolution imaging of biological surfaces
and processes. Extensions of the atomic force microscope are
the magnetic force microscope, which uses a magnetic tip to
image magnetic surfaces, and the electrostatic force
microscope, which measures the local dielectric polarizability
of a sample through the attractive force caused by applying
a voltage between the tip and the sample.

Sealed assembler lab
A general-purpose assembler system in a container permitting
only energy and information to be exchanged with the
environment.
2. A work space, containing assemblers, encapsulated in a
way that allows information to flow in and out but does not
allow the escape of assemblers or their products.

Self-assembly
The process of atoms and molecules adhering in a self-
regulating fashion, whereby specific atoms and molecules
bind to one another based on their size, shape, composition
or chemical properties. Molecular self-assembly is compatible
with traditional chip-making tools, making it attractive for
microelectronic applications. The goal is to have nanocircuits
self-assemble, enabling large-scale manufacturing of nanoscale
electronics.
2. In chemical solutions, self-assembly (also called Brownian
assembly) results from the random motion of molecules and
the affinity of their binding sites for one another. Also refers
to the joining of complementary surfaces in nanomolecular
interaction.

Self-repair
Indicating ability to heal itself without outside intervention.

Self-replication
More accurately labeled "exponential replication," self-replication refers to the process of growth or replication involving doubling within a given period.

Sentience Quotient
In the article "Xenopsychology" by Robert Freitas in Analog of April 1984 there is an interesting index called "Sentience quotient". It is based on: The sentience of an intelligence is roughly directly related to the amount of data it can process per unit time and inversely to the overall mass needed to do that processing. This would be something like baud/kilograms. And since that would rapidly turn into a real big number, base 10 logs are used. The "least sentient" would be one bit over the lifetime of the universe massing the entire known universe, or about -70. The "most sentient" is claimed to be +50. Homo sapiens are around +13, a Cray I is +9, a venus flytrap is a peak of +1 with plants generally -2.

Shape Memory Alloys
(SMA's) are a unique class of alloys which are able to "remember" their shape and are able to return to that shape even after being bent. The ability is known as the shape memory effect. ... This property has lead to many uses of SMA from orthodontics and coffee makers to methods of controlling aircraft and protecting buildings from earthquake damage. ... The first SMA to be discovered and the most commonly used is called Nitinol.

Shear modulus
Shear stress divided by shear strain; has the units of force per unit area.

Shear
A shear deformation is one that displaces successive layers of a material transversely with respect to one another, like a crooked stack of cards. Shear is a dimensionless quantity

measured by the ratio of the transverse displacement to the thickness over which it occurs.

Sigma bond

A covalent bond in which overlap between two atomic orbitals (e.g., of sp, sp_2, or sp_3 hybridization) produces a single bonding orbital in which the distribution of shared electrons has a roughly cylindrical symmetry about the axis linking the two atoms; see pi bond, single bond, double bond, triple bond. By themselves, sigma bonds present little barrier to rotation of one substructure with respect to another, although steric effects and cyclic structures may hinder or block rotation.

Single bond

A sigma bond having no associated pi bonds.

Singlet

An electronic state of a molecule in which all spins are paired; see doublet, triplet.

Singularity

Defined by Vernor Vinge as the "postulated point or short period in our future when our self-guided evolutionary development accelerates enormously (powered by nanotechnology, neuroscience, AI, and perhaps uploading) so that nothing beyond that time can reliably be conceived. ...a future time when societal, scientific and economic change is so fast we cannot even imagine what will happen from our present perspective, and when humanity will become posthumanity." Another definition is the singular time when technological development will be at its fastest. A grand evolutionary leap.

Sky Hook

A long, very strong, cable in orbit around a planet which rotates around its center of mass in such a way that when one end is closest to the ground, its relative velocity is almost zero. It would function as a kind of space elevator; shuttle craft would anchor to the end and then be lifted into orbit where they would be released. It is closely related to the idea of a beanstalk.

Smartdust

Also "Smartdust Motes" "...tiny, bottle-cap-shaped micro-machines fitted with wireless communication devices - that measure light and temperature [among other things, such as environmental monitoring, health, security, distributed processing and tracking - ed]. When clustered together, they automatically create highly flexible, low-power networks with applications ranging from climate-control systems to entertainment devices that interact with handheld computers."

Smart Materials

Here, materials and products capable of relatively complex behavior due to the incorporation of nanocomputers and nanomachines. Also used for products having some ability to respond to the environment. [NTN] If you combined microscopic motors, gears, levers, bearing, plates, sensors, power and communication cables, etc., with powerful microscopic computers, you have the makings of a new class of materials: "smart materials." Programmable smart materials could shape-shift into just about any desired object. A house made of smart materials would be quite useful and interesting. Imagine a wall changing color at your command, or making a window where their was none before.

Smart materials and products

Here, materials and products capable of relatively complex behavior due to the incorporation of nanocomputers and nanomachines. Also used for products having some ability to respond to the environment.

SNT

An abbreviation for structural nanotechnology; refers to integration of nanotech features into non-MNT products, also called nanomaterials.

Space Fountain

A vertical stream of magnetically accelerated pellets reaching out into space, where a station held aloft by its momentum reverses the direction and directs it towards a receiver on the ground. Essentially a simpler version of a Lofstrom loop. [I'm not sure who originated the idea, judging from Robert

Forward's indistinguishable from Magic it was a collaborative effort.

Spike, The
Another term for the singularity, suggested by Damien Broderick since the growth curves look almost like a spike as it is approached.

Spintronics
AKA: Quantum Spintronics, Magnetoelectronics, Spin Electronics. Electronic devices that exploit the spin of electrons as well as their charge. Unlike conventional electronics which is based on number of charges and their energy, and whose performance limited in speed and dissipation, spintronics is based on the direction of electron spin, and spin coupling, and is capable of much higher speed at much lower power. See our page on Spintronics.

sp, sp$_2$, sp$_3$
An isolated carbon atom has four valence orbitals: three mutually perpendicular p orbitals, each with a single nodal plane, and one spherically symmetric s orbital. A carbon atom in a typical molecule can be regarded as bonding with four orbitals consisting of weighted sums (termed hybrids) of these s and p orbitals. One common pattern has four equivalent orbitals, each formed by combining the three p orbitals with the s orbital; this is sp$_3$ hybridization. An sp$_3$ carbon atom forms four sigma bonds, usually in a roughly tetrahedral arrangement. Another common pattern has three equivalent orbitals formed by combining two p orbitals with the s orbital; this is termed sp$_2$ hybridization. An sp2 carbon atom forms three roughly coplanar sigma bonds, usually separated by ~120 , and one pi bond (or several fractional pi bonds). If a single p orbital is combined with the s orbital, the result is sp hybridization, forming two sigma bonds and two pi bonds (usually in a straight line). Atoms of other kinds (e.g., N and O) can hybridize in an analogous manner.

Species
In chemistry, a distinct kind of molecule, ion, or other structure.

Stable

Strictly speaking, a system is termed stable if no rearrangement of its parts can form a system of lower free energy. In practice, the term is used with an implicit proviso regarding the transformations to be considered. Hydrogen is not considered unstable merely because it is subject to nuclear fusion at extreme temperatures. A system is usually regarded as stable (more precisely, as kinetically stable) if its rate of transformation to a state of lower free energy is negligible (by some standard) under the ambient conditions. In nanomechanical systems, a structure can commonly be regarded as stable if it has an extremely low rate of transformations when subjected to its intended operating conditions.

Star Trek scenario

Someone builds potentially dangerous self-replicating devices that spread disastrously.

State

A physical system is said to be in a particular state when its physical properties fall within some particular range; the boundaries of the range defining a state depend on the problem under consideration. In a classical world, each point in phase space could be said to correspond to a distinct state. In the real world, time-invariant systems in quantum mechanics have a set of discrete states, particular superpositions of which constitute complete descriptions of the system. In practice, broader boundaries are usually drawn. A molecule is often said to be in a particular excited electronic state, regardless of its state of mechanical vibration. In nanomechanical systems, the PES often corresponds to a set of distinct potential wells, and all points in configuration space within a particular well can be regarded as one state. Definitions of state in the thermodynamics of bulk matter are analogous, but extremely coarse by these standards.

Statistical mechanics

Statistical mechanics treats the detailed state of a system (its quantum state or, in classical models, its position in phase space) as unknown and subject to statistical uncertainties; entropy is a measure of this uncertainty. Statistical mechanics describes the distribution of states in an equilibrium system at a given temperature (describing either the distribution of probabilities of quantum states or the probability density function in phase space), and can be used to derive thermodynamic properties from properties at the molecular level. These equilibrium results are useful in nanomechanical design.

Steric

Pertaining to the spatial relationships of atoms in a molecular structure, and in particular, to the space-filling properties of a molecule. If molecules were rigid and had hard surfaces, steric properties would merely be an opaque way of saying "shape"; a flexible side-chain, however, has definite steric properties but no fixed shape. Nanomechanical systems make extensive use of the steric properties of relatively rigid molecules, for which the term "shape" has essentially its conventional meaning so long as one remembers that the surface interactions are soft on small length-scales.

Steric hindrance

Slowing of the rate of a chemical reaction owing to the presence of structures on the reagents that mechanically interfere with the motions associated with the reaction, typically by obstructing the reaction site.

Stewart Platforms

A positional device. John Storrs info and links See also A New Family of Six Degree Of Freedom Positional Devices.

Stiffness

The stiffness of a system with respect to a deformation (e.g., the stiffness of a spring with respect to stretching) is the second derivative of the energy with respect to the corresponding displacement; this measures the curvature of the potential energy surface along a particular direction. Positive stiffness is associated with stability, and a large stiffness can result in a small positional uncertainty in the presence of thermal excitation. Negative stiffnesses correspond to unstable locations on the potential energy surface.

Alternative terms for stiffness include force gradient and rigidity.

STM

A scanning tunneling microscope.

Strain

In mechanical engineering, strain is a measure of the deformation resulting from stress (that is, force per unit area); the displacement of one point with respect to another, divided by their equilibrium separation in the absence of stress. In chemistry, a molecular fragment generally has some equilibrium geometry (bond lengths, interbond angles, etc.) when the rest of the molecular structure does not impose special constraints (e.g., bending bonds to form a small ring). Deviations from this equilibrium geometry are described as strain, and increase the energy of the molecule. Strain in the mechanical engineering sense causes strain in the chemical sense.

Stress

Force per unit area applied by one part of an object to another. Pressure is an isotropic compressive stress. Suspending a mass from a fiber places it in tensile stress. Gluing a layer of rubber between two plates and then sliding one over the other (while holding their separation constant) places the rubber in shear stress.

Structural volume

The interior of a diamondoid structure typically consists of a dense network of covalent bonds; a larger excluded volume, however, is determined by nonbonded repulsions at the surface. The structural volume corresponds to a region smaller than the excluded volume, chosen to make properties such as the strength and modulus nearly size independent by correcting for surface effects.

Superintelligence

An intellect that is much smarter than the best human brains in practically every field, including scientific creativity, general wisdom and social skills. This definition leaves open how the superintelligence is implemented: it could be a digital computer, an ensemble of networked computers, cultured cortical tissue or what have you. It also leaves open whether the superintelligence is conscious and has subjective experiences.

Superlattice Nanowire Pattern (transfer)

[SNAP] a technique for producing "Ultra High Density Nanowire Lattices and Circuits". See Researchers Discover How to Make the Smallest, Most Perfect, Densest Nanowire Lattices-And It's a SNAP. Superlattice Nanowire interwoven bundles of nanowires using substances with different compositions and properties.

Superlattices

Artificial metallic superlattices are multilayered thin films, prepared by alternately depositing two elements using vacuum deposition or sputtering techniques. A wide spectrum of elements and compounds are suitable for deposition into superlattice structures, and the range of properties displayed by the resulting superstructures is greatly dependent upon the properties of both individual lattices as well as the interaction between them.

Superposition

A quantum mechanical phenomena in which an object exists in more than one state simultaneously.

Synthesis

The production of a specific molecular structure by a series of chemical reactions.

Synthespian

An artificial actor, for example a 3D model animated by motion capture from a real actor or a computer program.

System

In scientific usage, usually equivalent to "a collection of matter and energy being analyzed as a unit." In engineering usage, usually equivalent to "a set of components working together to serve a set of purposes."

T

Technocyte

A nanoscale artificial device (especially a nanite) in the human bloodstream used for repairs, cancer protection, as an artificial immune system or for other uses.

Technofobics

Those who have a phobia to technology, and/or to advances in technology.

Temperature

A system in which internal vibrational modes have equilibrated with one another can be said to have a particular temperature. Two systems A and B are said to be at different temperatures if, when brought into contact, heat flows from (say) A to B, increasing the thermal energy of B at the expense of the thermal energy of A.

Terraform

To change the properties of a planet to make it more earthlike, making it possible for humans or other terrestrial organisms to live unaided on it, for example by changing atmospheric composition, pressure, temperature or the climate and introducing a self-sustaining ecosystem. This will most probably be a very long-term project, probably requiring self-replicating technology and megascale engineering. So far Venus and especially Mars looks as the most promising candidates for terraforming in the solar system.

Thermal energy

The internal energy present in a system as a result of the energy of thermally equilibrated vibrational modes and other motions (including both kinetic energy and molecular potential energy). The mean thermal energy of a classical harmonic oscillator is kT.

Thermal expansion coefficient

The rate of change of length with respect to temperature for a particular material.

Thermal fluctuations

The thermal energy of a system (or of a particular part or mode of motion in a system) has a mean value determined by the temperature and by the structure of the system. Statistical deviations about that mean are termed thermal fluctuations; these are of great importance in determining both rates of chemical reactions and error rates in nanomechanical systems.

Thermal Noise

The vibration and motion of atoms and molecules caused by the fact that they have a temperature above absolute zero. [RCM] Once used as an argument on why MNT could not work.

Thermodynamics

A field of study embracing energy conversion among various forms, including heat, work, and potential and kinetic energy.

Thermoelastic

Both stress and temperature changes alter the dimensions of an object having a finite stiffness and a nonzero thermal expansion coefficient. Applying a stress then produces a temperature change; this can result in a heat flow which then changes the stress: these are thermoelastic effects, and result in losses of free energy.

Thiol

An SH group, or a molecule containing one. Also known as a sulfhydryl or mercapto group.

Tight-receptor structures

A receptor structure in which a bound ligand of a particular kind is confined on all sides by repulsive interactions (note that favorable binding energies are compatible with repulsive forces). A tight-receptor structure discriminates strongly against all molecules larger than the target.

Top Down Molding

[AKA: mechanical nanotechnology] Carving and fabricating small materials and components by using larger objects such as our hands, tools and lasers, respectively. [NTN] Opposite of Bottom Up.

Transhuman

Someone actively preparing for becoming posthuman. Someone who is informed enough to see radical future possibilities and plans ahead for them, and who takes every current option for self-enhancement.

Transhumanism

Philosophies of life (such as Extropianism) that seek the continuation and acceleration of the evolution of intelligent life beyond its currently human form and human limitations by means of science and technology, guided by life-promoting values.

Transistor

The basic element in an integrated circuit. An on/off switch (consisting of three layers of a semiconductor material) that consists of a source (where electrons come from), a drain (where they go) and a gate that controls the flow of electrons through a channel that connects the source and the drain. There are two kinds of transistor, the bipolar transistor (also called the junction transistor), and the field effect transistor (FET).

Transition state

At the saddle point of a col linking two potential wells, the direction of maximum negative curvature defines the reaction coordinate; the transition state is a hypothetical system of reduced dimensionality, free to move only on a hypersurface perpendicular to the reaction coordinate at its point of maximum energy.

Transition state theory

Any of several theories that give approximate descriptions of chemical reaction rates based on the PES of the system, and in particular, on the properties of two potential wells and a transition state between them.

Tribology

study of friction, wear and lubrication of interacting surfaces.

Triple bond

A double bond is formed when a pi bond is superimposed on a single bond; adding a second pi bond results in a triple bond. The two pi bonds have perpendicular nodal planes, and their sum has roughly cylindrical symmetry, permitting rotation in much the same manner as a single bond.

Triplet

An electronic state of a molecule in which two spins are aligned. This term is derived from spectroscopy: a system of two aligned spins has three possible orientations with respect to a magnetic field; each has a different energy, resulting in sets of three field-dependent spectral lines (see doublet, singlet.)

TST

Transition state theory.

Tubeologist

Someone who knows their nanotubes inside and out, such as David Tom·nek.

Turing Test

Turing's proposed test for whether a machine is conscious (or intelligent, or aware): we communicate via text with it and with a hidden human. If we can't tell which of our partners in dialogue is the human, we say the computer is conscious.

Tunneling

A classical particle or system could not penetrate regions in which its energy would be negative, that is, barrier regions in which the potential energy is greater than the system energy. In the real world, however, a wave function of significant amplitude may extend into and beyond such a region. If the wave function extends into another region of positive energy, the barrier is crossed with some probability; this process is termed tunneling (since the barrier is penetrated rather than climbed).

Ubiquitous Computing

Also known as "embodied virtuality", "smart environment" and "ambient intelligence". Computers that are an integral, invisible part of people's lives. In some ways the opposite of virtual reality, in which the user is absorbed into the computational world. With ubiquitous computing, computers take into account the human world rather than requiring humans to enter into the computer's methods of working.

Unimolecular

Occurring to or within a single molecule; like intramolecular, but can refer to fragmentation reactions.

Universal Assembler

Uses raw atoms and molecules to construct consumer goods, and is pollution free. Can be programmed to build anything that is composed of atoms and consistent with the rules of chemical stability. Eric Drexler talks about these assemblers as nanorobots with telescoping manipulator arms that are capable of picking up individual atoms, and combining them however they are programmed.

Universal Constructor

A machine capable of constructing anything that can be constructed. The physical analog of a "universal computer", which can perform any computation.

Uplift
> To increase the intelligence and help develop a culture of a previously non- or near-intelligent species.

Upload
> (a) To transfer the consciousness and mental structure of a person from a biological matrix to an electronic or informational matrix (this assumes that the strong AI postulate holds). The term "Downloading" is also sometimes used, mainly to denote transferring the mind to a slower or less spacious matrix. (b) The resulting infomorph person. [The origin of the term is uncertain, but obviously based on the computer technology term 'uploading' (loading data into a mainframe computer).]

Utility Fog
> Objects formed of "intelligent" polymorphic (able to change shape) substances, typically having an octet truss structure.

Single Foglet

> "Imagine a microscopic robot. It has a body about the size of a human cell and 12 arms sticking out in all directions. A bucketfull of such robots might form a 'robot crystal' by linking their arms up into a lattice structure. Now take a room, with people, furniture, and other objects in it -- it's still mostly empty air. Fill the air completely full of robots. The robots are called Foglets and the substance they form is Utility Fog, which may have many useful medical applications. And when a number of utility foglets hold hands with their neighbors, they form a reconfigurable array of 'smart matter.'"

Vasculoid

The vasculoid [concept] is a single, complex, multisegmented nanotechnological medical robotic system capable of duplicating all essential thermal and biochemical transport functions of the blood, including circulation of respiratory gases, glucose, hormones, cytokines, waste products, and cellular components. [RAF CJP] See Vasculoid: A Personal Nanomedical Appliance to Replace Human Blood. Robert A. Freitas Jr. & Christopher J. Phoenix Transhumanist.com April 2002

Virtual reality system

A combination of computer and interface devices (goggles, gloves, etc.) that presents a user with the illusion of being in a three dimensional world of computer-generated objects.

Virtual Nanomedicine

Using VR to perform surgery and other functions inside the body.

Virus

A parasite (consisting primarily of genetic material) that invades cells and takes over their molecular machinery in order to copy itself.

Von Neumann Machine

(pronounced von noi-man) A machine which is able to build

a working copy of itself using materials in its environment. This is often proposed as a cheap way to mine or colonize the entire solar system or galaxy.

VON Neumann Probe

A von Neumann Machine able to move over interstellar or interplanetary distances and to utilize local materials to build new copies of itself. Such probes could be used to set up new colonies, perform megascale engineering or explore the universe.

Wet Nanotechnology

The study of biological systems that exist primarily in a water environment. The functional nanometer-scale structures of interest here are genetic material, membranes, enzymes and other cellular components. The success of this nanotechnology is amply demonstrated by the existence of living organisms whose form, function, and evolution are governed by the interactions of nanometer-scale structures.

Zeptosecond

one-billion-trillionth of a second, or 10 -21 second. Because nuclear movement takes place so quickly, scientists would need a pulse of light lasting just one zeptosecond to observe them. Johns Hopkins University

Zettatechnology

In which zetta means 1021, referring to the typical number of distinct designed parts in a product made by the systems we envision (molecular, mature, or molecular-manufacturing-based nanotechnology). The term refers to the implemented technology and its products, rather than to intermediate steps on the pathway.